Contents

Introduction

The *Mental Warm-up Activities* provide a structured scheme of work for developing mental mathematics strategies. The daily activities have been written to practice key mental maths skill, and address these using a variety of tactics:

- practising pre-requisite skills (e.g. partitioning numbers: 8 is 7 and 1, 6 and 2, 5 and 3, 4 and 4)
- building on two or more of these skills to develop a new strategy (e.g. adding 17 + 8 by partitioning 8 into 3 and 5, and knowing that 17 + 3 = 20)
- practising and extending known strategies (e.g. 127 + 8 =)
- using known strategies as pre-requisites for a new set of strategies, (e.g. related to a different operation)
- developing a 'memory bank' of key facts (e.g. addition bonds to 10, doubles to 10)
- using key facts to develop further strategies (e.g. 6 + 6 = 12 so 6 + 7 = 13)

How to use the book

For each Number Unit there are five whole class activities. Some of these relate directly to skills or sub-skills for that Unit. Some activities practise more general skills, and these will develop in strands throughout the book, leading into the next book in the series (a skills chart outlining these developments is included on pages 66 to 70). Taken together this bank of activities will develop all the strategies and techniques included in the National Framework for Numeracy.

Each day, either as a warm-up to the main maths lesson, or as a separate ten-minutes mental maths activity, select one of the activities provided.

The activities are of three types:

open-ended These are activities where there may be several ways of getting a 'right' answer. Often a key benefit of the activity will be the discussion which the children have with you and each other about which strategies they have used. This is a good opportunity to go through several different ways of doing something with the whole class, so that different methods or techniques are shared and discussed.

closed These activities have one correct answer and usually, one preferred strategy to use. So, for example, when adding 9 to a 2-digit number, the activity may practise the specific technique of adding 10 and taking one away.

memorising These activities are designed to help children memorise a particular set of number facts, e.g. doubles of numbers to 10, addition bonds. Eventually each child will have a set of memorised facts that they know by heart. Certain key activities appear several times during the book to help reinforce these skills.

generic activities A large number of the activities use similar formats and structures from Unit to Unit, and children will become familiar with these. These 'generic' activities are described in more detail on pages iv–vi.

Also included in each section are a 'word of the week', a 'number of the week' and occasionally 'a shape of the week'. These can be used to develop children's use of the language and vocabulary of number both spoken ('tell me something about this week's number') and written ('write three things about this week's shape').

The number of the week can be used to develop mental dexterity, consolidate concepts and skills studied in a given Number Unit, and to develop the use and understanding of the language of number. For each number some sample tasks and facts are given.

The word of the week can be used to develop use and understanding of the vocabulary of mathematics, and to consolidate language associated with the Unit being studied. Sometimes the word of the week relates to vocabulary in the relevant Unit, sometimes the word is included to rehearse vocabulary met in the past. Children should be encouraged to both hear the word being used in different contexts, and to use the word in responses and statements.

The shape of the week can be used to increase awareness of the properties of shape and space, and to encourage the use of the associated language.

Working partners At the beginning of the year (or each term), place the children in pairs as 'working partners'. The pairs do not necessarily have to be matched in ability – two children of different abilities can help each other. Over time the children will become used to working together, and a 'regular' partner will save you time when setting up the activities.

Generic Activities

Many of the activities throughout this book follow common formats and structures. This will enable you to set up and run a particular activity quickly, and over time, the children will become used to the 'rules' involved. The 'generic' activities are described here in more detail.

Open the box

- Draw a grid on the board and write a number in each space.
- Cover each number with a piece of Blu-tacked card. Write a number on the card that relates in some way to the number beneath (e.g. ten more, double).
- Choose a child to choose a card and perform some operation on the number.
- Reveal the answer by removing the card.

Bingo

- The children work with their partners. They write several 'bingo' numbers on a piece of paper, circling each one. The numbers should match a certain criterion (e.g. less than 10).
- The teacher generates numbers at random (e.g. by selecting cards from a shuffled set).
- The teacher chooses a child to perform an operation on the card (e.g. number bonds to ten).
- The children can cross out one of their 'bingo' numbers if it matches the answer.
- The first pair to cross out all their numbers wins.

Table timer

- Draw a table on the board with about ten rows and three columns (this will vary from activity to activity).
- Write numbers at random in the first column.
- Children copy the grid.
- They operate on the numbers (e.g. multiplying by 6) and write the answers in the appropriate column.
- Go through the questions at the end as a class, asking different children for their answers.
- This activity appears throughout the year, and you may wish to keep track of children's scores and times.

Grid operations

- Draw a grid on the board and write a number in each space.
- The children copy the empty gird, performing an operation on each number before entering it in their grid.
- Go through the grid on the board, asking different children for their answers.

Twenty questions

- Read out twenty mental mathematics questions covering a variety of topics.
- Write each on the board as you read it.
- Allow about 30 seconds before moving on to the next question.
- Go through the questions at the end as a class, asking different children for their answers.
- This activity appears throughout the year, and you may wish to keep track of children's scores and times.

Show me

- The children work with their partners.
- Give each pair a set of number cards (0 to 9).
- Read out a range of tasks relating to a particular topic (e.g. 4-digit numbers, addition).
- The pairs match each answer using the cards, placing them face up on the table.

Three-in-a-row

- Divide the class into three or four teams, and give each team a small number grid: 1 to 100 (Resource Pack PCM) and some counters.
- Have a large number grid: 1 to 100 on display.
- Set a task (e.g. a subtraction) with reference to the large grid, and choose a child from one team to answer it.
- If that child answers correctly, their team can cover the answer on their small grid with a counter.
- Continue, asking a child from each team in turn.
- The winning team is the first to place three counters in any one row or column.

Codes

- The children work with their partners.
- Give each pair a set of number cards (0 to 9).
- Write on the board a series of operations, in which some digits have been replaced by letters.
- Explain that each letter stands for one digit only.
- Allow the children five or ten minutes to work on a solution to the 'code'.
- Discuss the solutions and methods as a class.

Make me

- Write two sets of numbers on the board: one set in triangles and one in circles.
- The children perform operations on the first set of numbers to try and make numbers in the second set.
- Allow about ten minutes then discuss the different answers.
- How many different ways are there?

All wrong

- Write ten equations on the board, all of which are incorrect.
- Point to each equation in turn.
- Ask several children why the equation is incorrect, and what the correct answer should be.
- Repeat for each equation.

N1 Number

Bingo

Addition bonds to 100
Number cards (5, 10, 15, ... 100)
Each pair writes five bingo numbers that are
multiples of 5 up to 100.
Select a card at random, hold it up and read it aloud.
Choose a child to say the addition bond to 100.
Any pair with a matching number can cross it out.

35

10	65	40
80	25	

Table timer

Addition bonds to 20 and 100
Draw two tables with two
columns. In the first table write
numbers up to 20 at random in
the first column and in the
second table numbers up to 100.
Children copy the table, writing
the addition bond to 20 and the
addition bond to 100 in the
correct table. Time them.

	Makes 20
17	3
6	
11	

	Makes 100
44	56
80	
19	

Missing numbers

Counting 5-digit numbers
Write ten sequences of 5-digit
numbers on the board, with
several numbers missing
from each.
Point to a missing number and
choose a child to say what it is.
Repeat for each missing number.

11001, 11002, ☐, 11004,
43329, ☐, 43331, 43332
56048, ☐, ☐, ☐
85998, 85999, ☐, ☐

Open the box

Counting on one from a 5-digit number
Draw a 2 × 5 grid on the board. Cover each space with a 5-digit number,
and underneath write the number 1 more.
Choose a child to point to a box and say the number 1 more.
Check with the class.
The child can 'open the box', to reveal the answer.

Make me

Adding, subtracting, multiplying
Write 3000, 5, 10, 463, 20 000, 90 on the board each in a triangle.
Write 27 558, 45 553, 113 373, 107 553, 33 373 on the board, each in a circle.
The children can combine any or all of the triangle numbers by adding, subtracting or multiplying.
Can they make any of the circle numbers? Allow ten minutes.
Discuss the different answers.

Number of the week

Sample tasks
• Read the number.
• Say how many hundreds, thousands, tens, ...
• Read the number if the digits are reversed.
• Say different numbers using the same five digits in different orders.

Sample facts
• it is 50 000 when rounded to its nearest thousand
• it is 418 short of 48 000
• its digit total is 26

Word of the week

Sample tasks
• Are these **consecutive** numbers: 4, 5, 6, 8, 9? No, they are not **consecutive** – 7 is missing.
• Put these numbers in **consecutive** order: 4, 2, 5, 6, 3. In **consecutive** order they are 2, 3, 4, 5, 6.
• Which three **consecutive** numbers have a total of 15? The **consecutive** numbers are 4, 5, 6.

Sample facts
• 3, 4, 5, 6 are **consecutive**
• all odd numbers greater than 2 are the total of two **consecutive** numbers
• 2, 4, 6, 8 are **consecutive** even numbers

N2 Decimals

Grid multiplication

Multiplying by 8
Draw a 2 × 5 grid on the board, with a number (up to 12) in each space.
Children copy the grid, multiplying each number by 8.
When the grid is complete, point to each space in turn, asking a
different child to say their answer.
Repeat for multiplying by 9, 7, 6, ...

Show me 🗣️

Decimals (hundredths)
Number cards (0 to 9), one set per pair
Set the children tasks where they have to match a particular criterion
using the cards. For example:
Show me 0.25, 0.5, 0.75, 1.5, 1.25, 1.75, 0.1
*Show me a decimal equivalent to: one quarter, one half, three and two tenths,
four and eight hundredths, 63%, 89%, ...*

Missing numbers

Counting decimal numbers
Write ten sequences of decimal
numbers (tenths) on the board. Replace
some of the digits with a '?'.
Point to a missing digit and choose a
child to say what it is.
Repeat for each missing digit.

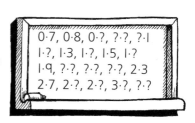

0·7, 0·8, 0·?, ?·?, ?·1
1·?, 1·3, 1·?, 1·5, 1·?
1·9, ?·?, ?·?, ?·?, 2·3
2·7, 2·?, 2·?, 3·?, ?·?

Three in a row

Subtracting one 2-digit number from another by counting on
**Four small number grids (1 to 100), counters, large number grid
(1 to 100)**
Divide the class into four teams, and give each team a number grid and
some counters.
Point to two 2-digit numbers on the large grid (within ten places of each
other, e.g. 38 and 46). Choose a child to say the difference between the
two numbers.
If the child answers correctly the team can cover either of the two
numbers on their grid with a counter.
Continue, choosing a child from each team in turn.
The winner is the first team to place three counters in any row or
column.

Twenty questions

Place-value, adding, subtracting, doubling, multiplying, halving

Read out these numbered questions, writing them on the board as you read them. Allow about 30 seconds for children to write the answer to each, before moving on to the next question.

1 Write $\frac{3}{10}$ as a decimal.   **2** What is two less than 2000?   **3** $120 \div 2$

4 $5 \times 60 =$ **5** $8.9 + 2 =$ **6** $6.4 + 1.9 =$

7 $7 + ? = 10$ **8** $36 + ? = 100$ **9** $620 + ? = 1000$

10 $81 - 7 =$ **11** $163 - 7 =$ **12** $456 - 156 =$

13 How many fives in 200?   **14** 2×45 **15** $32 \times 4 =$

16 $35 + 36 =$ **17** $\frac{2}{5}$ of $30 =$ **18** 25% of $400 =$

19 £1.50 shared amongst 6 people is?   **20** $3 \times 5 \times 6 =$

Number of the week	**Sample tasks** • Say the number as a fraction. • What is its nearest whole number, and how far is it away? • What must be added to it to make 10?	**Sample facts** • it is between 3 and 4 • it is 36 tenths • it is double 1.8
Word of the week	**Sample tasks** • How many digits in one **million**? One **million** has 7 digits: 1 000 000. • How many thousands is a **million**? A **million** is one thousand thousands. • What is 10 less than a **million**? 10 less than a **million** is 999 990.	**Sample facts** • a person who has one **million** pounds is called a millionaire • half a **million** is 500 thousands • there are one **million** (one thousand thousands) millimetres in a kilometre
Shape of the week	**Sample facts** • it is a 3-d shape • it can be hollow or solid • it has two identical 'end-pieces', and you can 'slice' through it to make the	same end-piece (cross-section) • a prism whose end-pieces are triangles is called a triangular prism • a cuboid is a prism

N3 Decimals

Table timer

Multiplying by 2, 4 and 8
Draw a table with four columns. In the first
column write 2-digit numbers at random.
Children copy the table, multiplying by 2
and writing the answer in the second column,
by 4 in the third column and by 8 in the
fourth column. Time them.

	x 2	x 4	x 8
14			
32			
26			

Target number

Adding, multiplying and dividing
Write a decimal target number on the board, e.g. 5.66.
Each pair works to find a way of making the target by doubling then
adding or subtracting (e.g. double 2.5 = 5, 5 + 0.66 = 5.66).
Ask different pairs for their solutions. Discuss the different ways.
Repeat for a new target.

All wrong

Decimal fractions
Write ten decimals on the board,
with their fraction equivalents.
Ensure that they are all incorrect.
Point to an equation, and choose
several children to say why it is
incorrect, and what the correct
answer should be.
Repeat for each equation.

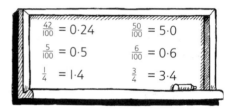

$$\frac{42}{100} = 0.24 \qquad \frac{50}{100} = 5.0$$
$$\frac{5}{100} = 0.5 \qquad \frac{6}{100} = 0.6$$
$$\frac{1}{4} = 1.4 \qquad \frac{3}{4} = 3.4$$

Open the box

Counting back one hundredth from a decimal number
Draw a 2 × 5 grid on the board. Cover each space with a decimal
number (hundredths), and underneath write the number 1 hundredth
less. Choose a child to point to a box and say the number 1 hundredth
less. Check with the class.
The child can 'open the box', to reveal the answer.

Codes

Addition bonds to 100

Number cards (0 to 9), one set per pair

Write this coded sequence of decimals on the board:

o.m, o.a, o.n, s.o, s.s, s.i, s.d, s.r, s.m, s.a, p.o, p.s, p.p,
p.d, p.e, p.r, p.m, p.a, p.n, i.o, i.s

Each digit (0 to 9) is represented by one letter only.
0 is represented by o. Some numbers are missing.
Allow the children five minutes to explore the code.
Discuss the solution.

Number of the week

Sample tasks

- Say the number as a fraction.
- How many hundredths do we need to add to it to make 2?
- What is its nearest tenth/ nearest whole number?
- Show me our number on the number line.

Sample facts

- it is between 1 and 2; between 1.3 and 1.4
- it is half of 2.76
- it is 1 whole and 38 hundredths; 1 whole 3 tenths and 8 hundredths; 138 hundredths

---

Word of the week

Sample tasks

- Say the first six **multiples** of 6. The **multiples** are; 6, 12, 18, 24, 30, 36.
- What is the fifth **multiple** of 9? The fifth **multiple** of 9 is 45.
- Which **multiple** is common to both 3 and 5? **Multiples** common to 3 and 5 are 15, 30, 45, ...

Sample facts

- **multiples** of 4 are all even
- **multiples** of 3 are alternately even and odd
- common **multiples** of 3 and 4 are **multiples** of 12

 Decimals

Grid rounding

Rounding decimals (tenths) to the nearest whole number
Draw a 2 × 5 grid on the board, with a decimal number (tenths) up to 12 in each space. Children copy the grid, rounding each decimal to the nearest whole number. When the grid is complete, point to each space in turn, asking a different child to say their answer.

Show me

Decimals (hundredths)
Number cards (0 to 9), one set per pair
Set the children tasks where they have to match a particular criterion using the cards. For example:
Show me 2.45, 5.16, 1.05, 6.23, 16.58, 11.8, 1.7, 0.9
Show me a decimal equivalent to: three and five tenths, six and forty-three hundredths, 58%, 34%, ...

Bingo

Rounding a decimal (hundredths) to the nearest whole number
Number cards (0 to 9)
Each pair writes five bingo numbers (0 to 10).
Select three cards at random. Make a decimal number (hundredths), hold it up and read it aloud. Choose a child to round to the nearest whole number. Any pair with a matching number can cross it out.

Make me

Rounding a decimal (hundredths) to the nearest tenth
Write 3.28, 4.55, 10.81, 1.46, 2.26 on the board, each in a triangle. Write 14.9, 8.7, 0.9, 8.7 on the board, each in a circle.
The children can combine any or

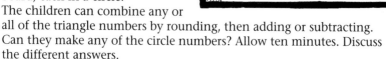

$3{\cdot}3 + 4{\cdot}6 + 1{\cdot}5 + 2{\cdot}3 = 11{\cdot}7$

$11{\cdot}7 - 10{\cdot}8 = 0{\cdot}9$

all of the triangle numbers by rounding, then adding or subtracting. Can they make any of the circle numbers? Allow ten minutes. Discuss the different answers.

Twenty questions

Place-value, adding, subtracting, doubling, multiplying, halving
Read out these numbered questions, writing them on the board as you read them.

Allow about 30 seconds for children to write the answer to each, before moving on to the next question.

1 Round 5.52 to the nearest tenth.
2 What is 2 more than 9998?
3 $450 \div 5 =$
4 $5 \times 23 =$
5 $59 + 41 =$
6 $56 \div 7 =$
7 $140 + 560 =$
8 $245 + 1200 =$
9 $55 + 56 + 57 =$
10 $37 - 18 =$
11 $137 - 16 =$
12 $532 - 132 =$
13 $823 - 624 =$
14 $265 - 15 =$
15 $361 - 99 =$
16 $\frac{2}{5}$ of 30 =
17 5% of 200 =
18 $69 \div 3 =$
19 $102 \div 3 =$
20 How many 50p coins in £50?

Number of the week

Sample tasks
• Round our number to its nearest tenth, and nearest whole number.
• Say a number which is more/less than our number.
• What is the value of each of the digits: 7, 9, 4.
• Show me our number on the number line.

Sample facts
• it is between 4 and 5
• it is one hundredth short of 4.8
• it is a decimal number with two decimal places

Word of the week

Sample tasks
• Name the **factors** of 12. The **factors** of 12 are: 1, 2, 3, 4, 6, 12.
• How many **factors** has 15? 15 has 4 **factors**: 1, 3, 5, 15.
• What are the common **factors** of 12 and 15. The common **factors** of 12 and 15 are 1 and 3.

Sample facts
• 1 is a **factor** of every number
• prime numbers have exactly 2 **factors**
• square numbers have an odd number of **factors**

Shape of the week

equilateral triangle

Sample facts
• an equilateral triangle has all three sides the same length
• each angle of an equilateral triangle is 60°
• equilateral triangles tessellate
• equilateral triangles have three lines of symmetry
• equilateral triangles have rotational symmetry of order 3

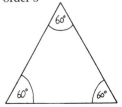

N5 Addition

Table timer

Addition bonds to 50 and 100
Draw two tables with two columns. In the first table write numbers up to 50 at random in the first column and in the second table write numbers up to 100 at random.

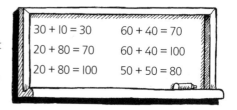

	Make 50
20	
41	

	Make 100
65	
32	

Children copy the table, writing the addition bond to 50, and the addition bond to 100 in the correct table. Time them.

All wrong

Adding two 2-digit multiples of 10
Write ten additions of two 2-digit multiples of 10 on the board. Ensure that they are all incorrect. Point to an addition, and choose several children to say why it is incorrect, and what the correct

30 + 10 = 30	60 + 40 = 70
20 + 80 = 70	60 + 40 = 100
20 + 80 = 100	50 + 50 = 80

answer should be. Repeat for each addition.

Bingo

Addition bonds to 100
Number cards (5, 10, 15, ... 100)
Each pair writes five bingo numbers that are multiples of 5 up to 100.
Select a card at random, hold it up and read it aloud.
Choose a child to say the addition bond to 100.
Any pair with a matching number can cross it out.

Open the box

Addition bonds to 1000
Draw a 2 × 5 grid on the board. Cover each space with a 3-digit multiple of 10, and underneath write its addition bond to 1000.
Choose a child to point to a box and say the addition bond to 1000 (they can work on the board to help).
Check with the class.
The child can 'open the box', to reveal the answer.

o 1 2 3 4 5 6 7 8 9
o a r s e n l f c d.

Codes

Adding multiples of 10

Number cards (0 to 9), one set per pair

Write these coded additions on the board:

noo + noo = aooo, rno + rno = noo, sno + sno = foo, eno + eno = doo,
lso + sfo = aooo, rco + fro = aooo, eno + nno = aooo, ado + cao = aooo

Each digit (0 to 9) is represented by one letter only.

0 is represented by o.

Allow the children five minutes to explore the code.

Discuss the solution.

Number of the week

1000

Sample tasks
- What must be added to 300, 700, 100, ...to make our number?
- What must be added to 450, 850, 350, 420, ... to make our number?
- What is the result of subtracting 360, 580, 190, ... from our number?

Sample facts
- it is ten hundreds
- it is the number of metres in a kilometre and grams in a kilogram
- it is a multiple of 10, 20, 50, 100, and 500

Word of the week

hundredth

Sample tasks
- How long is one **hundredth** of a metre? One **hundredth** of a metre is one centimetre.
- What percentage is twenty-three **hundredths**? 23 **hundredths** is 23%.
- How many **hundredths** in 0.34? 34 **hundredths** or 3 tenths and 4 **hundredths**.

Sample facts
- one tenth is ten **hundredths**
- the second decimal place in 2.35 shows the number of **hundredths**, i.e. 5 hundredths
- one **hundredth** of a million is 10 000

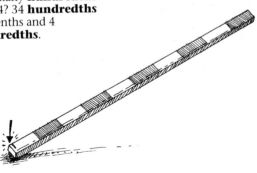

#

Grid rounding

Rounding a 3-digit number to the nearest hundred
Draw a 2 × 5 grid on the board, with a 3-digit number in each space.
Children copy the grid, rounding each number to the nearest hundred.
When the grid is complete, point to each space in turn, asking a
different child to say their answer.

Show me

Adding several 1-digit numbers
Number cards (0 to 9), one set per pair
Set the children tasks where they have to match a particular criterion
using the cards. For example:
Show me three cards that make 8, 12, 20
Show me four cards that make 10, 15, 21, ...

Missing numbers

*Estimating the addition of three 2- or
3-digit numbers*
Write ten additions on the board – use
three 2- or 3-digit numbers. In each
case replace one of the numbers, or the
answer with a '?'. Point to a missing

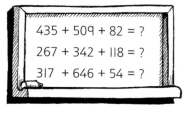

435 + 509 + 82 = ?
267 + 342 + 118 = ?
317 + 646 + 54 = ?

number and choose a child to estimate what it is. Check with the class.
Repeat for each missing number.

Target number

*Estimating the addition of two 4-digit
numbers*
Write a target number on the board,
e.g. 8000. Each pair works to find a way
of making the target by rounding two
4-digit numbers, then adding. Ask

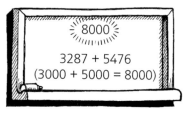

8000

3287 + 5476
(3000 + 5000 = 8000)

different pairs for their solutions. Discuss the different ways. Repeat for
a new target.

Twenty questions

Place-value, adding, subtracting, doubling, multiplying, halving
Read out these numbered questions, writing them on the board as you
read them. Allow about 30 seconds for children to write the answer to
each, before moving on to the next question.

1 Four times ten thousand. 2 What is four more than 10 098?

3 $51 \times 3 =$
4 $2.5 + 4.5 =$
5 $3.4 + 6.6 =$

6 $5.1 - 1.9 =$
7 $71 + ? = 100$
8 $280 + ? = 1000$

9 $245 + 755 =$
10 $91 - 6 =,$
11 $174 - 16 =$

12 $527 - 199 =$
13 $75 \div 5 =$
14 $45 \div 9 =$

15 $41 \times 4 =$
16 $65 + 66 =$
17 $\frac{3}{7}$ of $35 =$

18 2% of $200 =$
19 $23 + 24 + 25 + 26 =$

20 $3 + 6 + 7 + 2 + 9 + 8 =$

Number of the week

Sample tasks
- Round our number to its nearest 10, 100 and 1000.
- Estimate the total when our number is added to 3870, 4190, ...
- Read the number, then read it when the four digits are rearranged.

Sample facts
- it has a digit total of 11
- it can be divided by 2, but not by 3 or 4
- it is 838 less than 3000

Word of the week

Sample tasks
- Say the first 10 **prime numbers**. The first 10 **prime numbers** are: 2, 3, 5, 7, 11, 13, 17, 19, 23, 29.
- What is the nearest **prime number** to 30? The nearest **prime number** is 31 or 29.
- Why is 27 not a **prime number**? It is not **prime** because it can be divided by 3 and 9.

Sample facts
- **prime numbers** have exactly 2 factors
- 2 is the only even **prime number**
- apart from 2 and 3, all **prime numbers** are next to (adjacent to) a multiple of 6

Shape of the week

octagon, octagonal

Sample facts
- an octagon is a polygon with 8 sides
- an octagon has 8 angles
- if an octagon has equal angles and equal sides, then it is called a regular octagon
- some boxes are octagonal prisms
- 'oct' means eight e.g. an octopus has 8 legs

N7 Number

Table timer

Addition bonds to 100 and 1000
Draw two tables with two columns.
In the first table write numbers up
to 100 at random in the first
column. In the second table write
3-digit multiples of 10 at random.
Children copy the table, writing
the addition bond to 100 and the
addition bond to 1000 in the correct table. Time them.

	Make 100
40	
66	
79	

	Make 1000
130	
670	
210	

Show me

Decimals (hundredths)
Number cards (0 to 9), one set per pair
Set the children tasks where they have to match a particular criterion
using the cards. For example:
Show me a decimal number more than 1.30, 1.81, 3.45
Show me a decimal number less than 4.86, 3.21, 4.01
Show me a decimal number between 1.1 and 1.2, 3.45 and 3.5
Show me one quarter of 1.6, one half of 1.8, one quarter of 2.0
Show me 50% of 1.5, 25% of 2.4, ...

All wrong

Adding positive and negative numbers
Write ten additions on the
board – one positive and one
negative number. Ensure that
they are all incorrect.

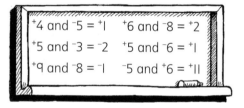

Point to an addition, and choose several children to say why it is
incorrect, and what the correct answer should be.
Repeat for each addition.

Open the box

Adding positive and negative numbers
Draw a 2 × 5 grid on the board. Cover each space with an addition of a
positive and a negative number. Underneath write the answer.
Choose a child to point to a box and say the answer.
Check with the class. The child can 'open the box', to reveal the answer.

$[(15 \times 5) + 17] \times 2 = 184$ $(15 \times 2) + (5 \times 12) + 17 = 107$
$(15 \times 5) + (2 \times 17) + 12 = 121$

Make me

Adding and multiplying
Write 15, 5, 12, 17, 2 on the board, each in a triangle.
Write 121, 107, 184, 305 on the board, each in a circle.
The children can combine any or all of the triangle numbers by adding or multiplying.
Can they make any of the circle numbers? Allow ten minutes.
Discuss the different answers.

Number of the week

Sample tasks
• Count in ones, twos, ... forwards and backwards from our number.
• Add our number to ⁺4, ⁺1, ⁻5, 0, ...
• What must be added to ⁺5, ⁻3, ⁺1, ... to make our number?

Sample facts
• it is between ⁻5 and ⁻3
• it is ⁺5 add ⁻9, ⁻3 add ⁻1, ⁻7 add ⁺3
• it is 3 less than ⁻1, 5 more than ⁻9

Word of the week

treble

Sample tasks
• What is **treble** 5? **Treble** 5 is 15.
• What number do you have to **treble** to make 45? **Treble** 15 is 45.
• What **trebles** match a double? **Treble** 6 matches double 9.

Sample facts
• **trebling** is multiplying by 3
• **treble** 10 is the same as double 15
• to find the total number of sides on 9 triangles, you **treble** 9

N8 Multiplication

Table timer

Multiplying by 4, 8 and 16
Draw a table with four columns. In the first
column write numbers up to 12 at random.
Children copy the table, multiplying by 4 and
writing the answer in the second column, by 8
in the third column and by 16 in the fourth
column. They can use doubling to help.
Time them.

	x 4	x 8	x 16
1			
6			
12			

Bingo

Multiplication facts up to 10 × 10
Number cards (3 to 9)
Each pair writes five bingo numbers that are the answers to
multiplication facts (from 3 × 4 to 8 × 9).
Select two cards at random, hold them up and read them aloud.
Choose a child to multiply the cards together and say the answer.
Any pair with a matching number can cross it out.
The first pair to cross out three numbers is the winner.

Missing numbers

*Multiplying a 3-digit number by
2 or 3*
Write ten multiplications of a
3-digit number by 2 or 3 on the
board. In each case replace
some of the digits of the answer

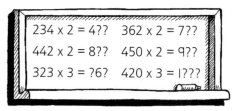

234 x 2 = 4??   362 x 2 = 7??
442 x 2 = 8??   450 x 2 = 9??
323 x 3 = ?6?   420 x 3 = 1???

with a '?'. Point to a missing digit and choose a child to say what it is.
Repeat for each missing digit.

Target number

Multiplying, adding, subtracting
Write a target number on the board, e.g. 80.
Each pair works to find a way of making the target by multiplying (one
1-digit number by another) then adding or subtracting a number less
than 25 (e.g. 7 × 9 = 63, 63 + 17 = 80).
Ask different pairs for their solutions. Discuss the different ways.
Repeat for a new target.

Twenty questions

Place-value, adding, subtracting, doubling, multiplying, halving

Read out these numbered questions, writing them on the board as you read them. Allow about 30 seconds for children to write the answer to each, before moving on to the next question.

1 What is 0.02 more than 3.99? **2** What is 0.02 less than 1.01?

3 $6 \times 8 =$ **4** $3 \times 25 =$ **5** $3 \times 2.4 =$

6 $6.2 - 4.2 =$ **7** $6.2 - 4.3 =$ **8** $1892 + 1200 =$

9 double 45   **10** double 46   **11** halve 50

12 halve 56   **13** $24 + 25 + 26 + 27 =$ **14** $7 \times 8 =$

15 $7 \times 16 =$ **16** What is 8 squared?   **17** $\frac{5}{6}$ of $36 =$

18 20% of 50 =   **19** Round 5.51 to the nearest whole number.

20 Write three hundredths as a decimal.

Number of the week

Sample tasks
- Is our number a multiple of 2, of 3, of 4, of 5, ...?
- Count in 2s, 3s, 4s, 5s, forwards and backwards from our number.
- Say some multiples of our number, e.g. 60, 180, 300.

Sample facts
- it is the number of days in September, April, June and November
- it is a multiple of 2, 3, 5, 6, 10, 15, 30
- it has 8 factors: 1, 2, 3, 5, 6, 10, 15, 30

Word of the week

Sample tasks
- What is the **remainder** when dividing 31 by 4? 31 divided by 4 leaves a **remainder** of 3.
- What do you have to divide 21 by to leave a **remainder** of 3? 21 divided by 6 or by 9.
- What fraction is a **remainder** of 1 when dividing by 10? The **remainder** is one tenth.

Sample facts
- when dividing by 5, the possible **remainders** are 0, 1, 2, 3, 4
- a **remainder** of 2 when dividing by 4 is equivalent to two quarters or one half
- prime numbers leave a **remainder** when divided by a number other than themselves or 1

Shape of the week

sector of a circle

Sample facts
- a sector of a circle is a 'slice' of a circle
- a pie chart is a circle divided into sectors
- if the angle of the sector is 90°, then the sector is a quarter-circle
- a sector has 3 sides: two radii and one arc of the circle
- a circle can be divided into six 60° sectors

N9 Division

Grid division

Dividing by 9

Draw a 2 × 5 grid on the board, with a 2- or 3-digit multiple of 9 in each space.

Children copy the grid, dividing each number by 9.

When the grid is complete, point to each space in turn, asking a different child to say their answer.

Repeat for dividing by 8, 7, 6, ...

All wrong

Dividing a 2-digit by a 1-digit number

Write ten divisions of a 2-digit by a 1-digit number on the board. Ensure that they are all incorrect. Point to a division, and choose several children to say why it is incorrect, and what the correct answer should be.

Repeat for each division.

$42 \div 6 = 8$ $66 \div 6 = 12$

$72 \div 9 = 9$ $35 \div 7 = 6$

$48 \div 6 = 9$ $64 \div 8 = 9$

Make me

Adding and multiplying

Write 8, 5, 12, 4, 6 on the board, each in a triangle. Write 504, 480, 1448, 288 on the board, each in a circle.

The children can combine any or all of the triangle numbers by adding or multiplying. Can they make any of the circle numbers?

Allow ten minutes. Discuss the different answers.

```
8 + 12 =  2 0
         x  6
         1 2 0
         x  4
         4 8 0
```

Open the box

Dividing a 2-digit by a 1-digit number

Draw a 2 × 5 grid on the board. Cover each space with a division of a 2-digit by a 1-digit number. Underneath write the answer.

Choose a child to point to a box and say the answer (they can work on the board to help).

Check with the class.

The child can 'open the box', to reveal the answer.

Codes

Multiplication facts up to 10 × 10

Number cards (0 to 9), one set per pair

Write these coded multiplications on the board:

    de × s = de   er × s = er   n × n = as   p × e = so   p × i = r

    p × d = a   m × a = er   i × n = pm   a × n = mp

Each digit (0 to 9) is represented by one letter only.

0 is represented by o.

Allow the children five minutes to explore the code.

Discuss the solution.

Number of the week

Sample tasks
- Say the first 10 multiples of our number, in order.
- What is the result of multiplying our number by 5, by 3, by 9, ...
- Divide 60, 36, 12, 6, 24, 66, 120, ... by our number.

Sample facts
- it is a common multiple of 2 and of 3
- it is the number of sides of a hexagon
- it is a factor of 12, of 36, of 18 and of 6

Word of the week

Sample tasks
- Hold up a metre stick. How many of these are needed to make a **kilometre**? 1000 metres is 1 **kilometre**.

- Approximately how many miles is 100 **kilometres**? 100 **kilometres** is approximately 60 miles.
- Show me one thousandth of a **kilometre**. This metre is one thousandth of a **kilometre**.

Sample facts
- a **kilometre** is a metric measure of distance
- 10 **kilometres** is about 6 miles
- 1 **kilometre** is 1000 metres and 1 metre is 1000 millimetres – so, 1 **kilometre** is 1 million millimetres

N10 Addition

Grid rounding

Rounding a decimal (tenths) to the nearest whole number

Draw a 2 × 5 grid on the board, with a decimal number(tenths), up to 20 in each space. Children copy the grid, rounding each decimal to the nearest whole number.

When the grid is complete, point to each space in turn, asking a different child to say their answer.

Show me

Adding to a decimal (hundredths) to make the next whole number

Number cards (0 to 9), one set per pair

Set the children tasks where they have to match a particular criterion using the cards. For example:

Show me the next whole number after 1.37, 2.45, 8.08

Show me the number that goes with 0.56, 3.31, 2.73, ... to make the next whole number

Show me the number that goes with 0.48, 0.32, 0.55, 0.87, 0.7, ... to make 1.00.

Missing numbers

Rounding a decimal (hundredths) to the nearest whole number

Write ten decimal numbers (tenths) on the board, and round each one to the nearest whole number. In each case replace one of the digits with a '?'.

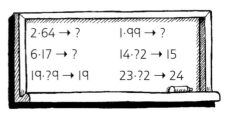

$2.64 \rightarrow ?$ $1.99 \rightarrow ?$

$6.17 \rightarrow ?$ $14.?2 \rightarrow 15$

$19.?9 \rightarrow 19$ $23.?2 \rightarrow 24$

Point to a missing digit and choose a child to say what it is.
Repeat for each missing digit.

Bingo

Estimating the addition of two decimals (tenths)

Two sets of number cards (0 to 9)

Each pair writes five bingo numbers(1 to 10).

Select two cards at random from each set. Make two decimal numbers (tenths) and write them on the board.

Choose a child to estimate the total. Check with the class.

Any pair with a matching number can cross it out.

Twenty questions

Place-value, adding, subtracting, doubling, multiplying, halving
Read out these numbered questions, writing them on the board as you read them. Allow about 30 seconds for children to write the answer to each, before moving on to the next question.

1 Write the approximate total of 2.3 + 5.8.
2 What is two hundredths less than 6.01?

3 $450 \div 5 =$	**4** $30 \times 5 =$	**5** $30 \times 50 =$
6 $5.2 - 4.2 =$	**7** $5.2 - 4.3 =$	**8** $2.5 \times 3 =$
9 $795 + 25 =$	**10** $123 - 7 =$	**11** $56 - 38 =$
12 $273 - 99 =$	**13** $54 + 23 + 19 =$	**14** $4 \times 6 =$
15 $6 \times 6 =$	**16** $38 + 39 =$	**17** $\frac{4}{5} \times 65 =$
18 30% of 80 =	**19** $2.5 + 9.5 =$	**20** How many twos in 380?

Number of the week

Sample tasks
• Add our number to 3, 7, 2, 14, ...
• Add our number to 2.3, 5.7, 1.8, 7.6, ...(by adding 1, then subtracting 0.1).
• Subtract our number from 5.5, 2.7, 6, 3.8, ... (by subtracting 1, then adding 0.1).

Sample facts
• it is nine tenths, or ninety hundredths
• it rounds to 1, when rounding to its nearest whole number
• it is 4.1 less than 5, 6.7 less than 7.6

Word of the week

Sample tasks
• If a circle has a diameter of 10 cm. What is its approximate **circumference**? Its approximate **circumference** is 30 cm.
• Estimate the **circumference** of this plate. I estimate its **circumference** to be 80 centimetres.

Sample facts
• **circumference** is the distance around the boundary of a circle
• the **circumference** is approximately 3 times (treble) the diameter
• the perimeter of a semi-circle is half the **circumference** of the circle plus its diameter

---

Shape of the week

Sample facts
• a quadrilateral is a 4-sided polygon
• squares and rectangles are quadrilaterals
• parallelograms and rhombus are quadrilaterals

• a trapezium is a quadrilateral with one pair of parallel sides
• a regular quadrilateral is a square

N11 Addition

All wrong

Addition bonds to 100
Write ten pairs of addition bonds
to 100 on the board. Ensure that
they are all incorrect.
Point to an addition, and choose
several children to say why it is
incorrect, and what the correct answer should be.
Repeat for each addition.

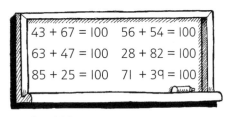

43 + 67 = 100	56 + 54 = 100
63 + 47 = 100	28 + 82 = 100
85 + 25 = 100	71 + 39 = 100

Open the box

Adding to a decimal (hundredths) to make the next whole number
Draw a 2 × 5 grid on the board. Cover each space with a decimal
number (with 5 hundredths), and underneath write the next whole
number. Choose a child to point to a box and say the next whole
number and what must be added to make it. Check with the class. The
child can 'open the box', to reveal the answer.

Three in a row

Adding near doubles
Four small number grids (1 to 100), counters, number cards (20 to 50)
Divide the class into four teams, and give each team a number grid and
some counters.
Select a card at random from the pile and write the number on the
board adding the number one more (e.g. 46 + 47). Choose a child to say
the answer. If the child answers correctly the team can cover that
number on their grid with a counter. Continue, choosing a child from
each team in turn.
The winners are the first to place three counters in any row or column.

Table timer

Addition bonds to 1.00 and 2.00
Draw two tables with two
columns. In the first table write
decimal numbers (tenths) up to
1 at random in the first column.
In the second table write
decimal numbers (with 0 or 5
hundredths) up to 2 at random.

	Make 1·00
0·6	
0·2	

	Make 2·00
1·30	
1·15	

Children copy the table, writing the addition bond to 1.00 and the
addition bond to 2.00 in the correct table. Time them.

Codes

Adding two decimals (tenths)

Number cards (0 to 9), one set per pair

Write these coded additions on the board:

s.b + j.a = 6.8	s.d + o.j = 6	j.j + d.d = 11	u.u + e.m = 12
s.b + o.e = b	m.n + o.a = e	u.e + a.j = d.s	

Each digit (0 to 9) is represented by one letter only.

0 is represented by o.

Allow the children five minutes to explore the code.

Discuss the solution.

Number of the week

Sample tasks
- What must be added to our number to make 10, 20, 5, ...?
- Round our number to its nearest whole number.
- How many tenths altogether in our number (i.e. 37).

Sample facts
- it is between $3\frac{1}{2}$ and 4
- it is half of 7.4
- it is 2.3 less than 6 and 5.3 less than 9

Word of the week

Sample tasks
- Approximately how many pints is 4 litres? 4 litres is approximately 8 **pints**.
- Approximately how many millilitres is 1 **pint**? 1 **pint** is approximately 500 millimetres.
- Drink half a **pint** of water.

Sample facts
- 1 **pint** is a little more than half a litre
- 8 **pints** are the same as 1 gallon
- A **pint** is an Imperial unit of measure of capacity

N12 Subtraction

Grid addition

Adding to a decimal (tenths) to make the next whole number
Draw a 2 × 5 grid on the board, with a decimal number (tenths) up to 20 in each space. Children copy the grid, adding to each number to make the next whole number. When the grid is complete, point to each space in turn, asking a different child to say their answer and what they added to make it.

Show me

Addition bonds to 100
Number cards (0 to 9), one set per pair
Set the children tasks where they have to match a particular criterion using the cards. For example:
Show me the number that goes with 52, 67, 82, 73, 38, ... to make 100.

Bingo

Adding to a decimal (hundredths) to make the next whole number
Number cards (0 to 9)
Each pair writes five bingo numbers (0 to 10).
Select three cards at random. Make a decimal number (hundredths), hold it up and read it aloud. Choose a child to add to it to make the next whole number (they can work on the board to help).
Any pair with a matching number can cross it out.

Make me

Adding and doubling decimal numbers (tenths)
Write 1.3, 7.5, 4.8, 2.6, 1.2 on the board, each in a triangle. Write 32.2, 24.7, 26 on the board, each in a circle. The children can combine any

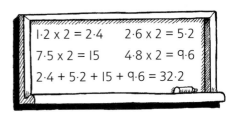

or all of the triangle numbers by adding or doubling. Can they make any of the circle numbers? Allow ten minutes. Discuss the different answers.

Twenty questions

Place-value, adding, subtracting, doubling, multiplying, halving
Read out these numbered questions, writing them on the board as you read them. Allow about 30 seconds for children to write the answer to each, before moving on to the next question.

1 $3.4 + ? = 4$	**2** $5.71 + ? = 8$	**3** $6.34 + 2.24 =$
4 $7 \times 12 =$	**5** $4.5 \times 2 =$	**6** $7.7 - 1.9 =$
7 $27 + ? = 100$	**8** $375 + ? = 1000$	**9** $432 + 299 =$
10 $133 - 34 =$	**11** $187 - 88 =$	**12** $329 + 330 =$
13 $58 + 59 + 60 =$	**14** double 36	**15** double 86
17 halve 34	**18** halve 56	**19** $4.9 + 4.9 =$
20 What is 0.03 less than 4.5?		

Number of the week

Sample tasks
- How many units, tenths, hundredths in our number?
- Show me our number on the number line.
- What must be added to our number to make the next whole number?

Sample facts
- it is 1 whole, 7 tenths and 6 hundredths
- it is 1 whole and 76 hundredths, 17 tenths and 6 hundredths or 176 hundredths
- it is a decimal number which has 2 decimal places

Word of the week

Sample tasks
- Draw a **square millimetre**. Here is a tiny **square millimetre**.
- How many **square millimetres** will fit inside a square centimetre. 100 **square millimetres** match 1 square centimetre.
- Draw a shape on the centimetre squared paper which is 400 **square millimetres**. This 2×2 square has an area of 400 **square millimetres**.

Sample facts
- a **square millimetre** is a unit for measuring area
- shorthand for **square millimetre** is mm^2
- there are 100 **square millimetres** in 1 square centimetre

Shape of the week

Sample facts
- a regular polygon is a polygon with equal sides and equal angles
- a square is a regular 4-sided polygon
- the vertices of a regular polygon lie on a circle whose centre is at the centre of the polygon
- an equilateral triangle is a regular 3-sided polygon
- a circle is a regular polygon with an infinite number of sides

N13 Multiplication

Table timer

Multiplying by 5, 10 and 100
Draw a table with four columns. In the first
column write numbers up to 100 at random.
Children copy the table, multiplying by 10
and writing the answer in the second column,
by 5 in the third column and by 100 in the
fourth column. Time them.

	x 10	x 5	x 100
70			
25			
10			

All wrong

*Multiplying by 10 and multiples
of 10*
Write ten multiplications on
the board – a 2-digit number by
10 or a multiple of 10. Ensure
that they are all incorrect.
Point to a multiplication, and

42 x 10 = 402	66 x 10 = 606
72 x 20 = 1044	65 x 20 = 1030
48 x 20 = 906	64 x 20 = 1208

choose several children to say why it is incorrect, and what the correct
answer should be. Repeat for each multiplication.

Missing numbers

Subtracting near multiples of 100 from a 3-digit number
Write ten subtractions on the board, of near multiples of 100 from
3-digit numbers. In each case replace some of the digits with a '?'.
Point to a missing digit and choose a child to say what it is.
Repeat for each missing digit.

264 – 99 = 1??	362 – 99 = 2??	448 – 199 = 2??
344 – 199 = 1??	428 – 198 = 2??	365 – 299 = ???
693 – 298 = 3??	724 – 197 = 5??	776 – 397 = ???

Open the box

Multiplying by 200, 300 and 400
Draw a 2 × 5 grid on the board. Cover each space with a multiplication
of a 1-digit number by 200, 300 or 400. Underneath write the answer.
Choose a child to point to a box and say the answer.
Check with the class.
The child can 'open the box', to reveal the answer.

d g f i a t c s h
1 3 7 8 5 6 4 9 2.

Codes

Multiplying multiples of 100
Number cards (0 to 9), one set per pair
Write these coded multiplications on the board:

goo × d = goo	doo × h = hoo	doo + doo = hoo
hoo × a = dooo	goo × h = too	foo × h = dcoo
goo × g = soo	goo × i = hcoo	ioo × f = atoo

Each digit (0 to 9) is represented by one letter only.
0 is represented by o.
Allow the children five minutes to explore the code.
Discuss the solution.

Number of the week

Sample tasks
- Say the multiples of our number, in order, up to 400.
- Multiply our number by 3, 8, 6, ...
- Multiply our number by 5, by 10, by 4, by 11, ...
- Continue halving from our number: 20, 10, 5, $2\frac{1}{2}$, $1\frac{1}{4}$, ...

Sample facts
- it is four 5s, two 10s, five 4s and ten 2s
- it is a multiple of 2, of 4, of 5, of 10 and of 20
- it is one score

Word of the week

cubic centimetre

Sample tasks
- Find a cube which has a volume of 1 **cubic centimetre**. This cube has a volume of 1 **cubic centimetre**.
- How many **cubic centimetres** can fit inside a 2 centimetre cube? Its volume is 8 **cubic centimetres**.
- Use the centimetre cubes to build a cuboid whose volume is 12 **cubic centimetres**. This cuboid has a volume of 12 **cubic centimetres**.

Sample facts
- a **cubic centimetre** is a unit for measuring volume
- there are $100 \times 100 \times 100$ (1 million) **cubic centimetres** in a cubic metre
- shorthand for **cubic centimetre** is cm³

N14 Multiplication

Grid multiplication

Multiplying a 2-digit by a 1-digit number
Draw a 2×5 grid on the board, with a 2-digit number (up to 50) in each
space. Children copy the grid, multiplying each number by 4.
When the grid is complete, point to each space in turn, asking a
different child to say their answer.
Repeat for multiplying by 3, 5, 6, ...

All wrong

*Multiplying a 2- or 3-digit number
by a 1-digit number*
Write ten multiplications on the
board – a 2- or 3-digit number by
a 1-digit number. Ensure that
they are all incorrect.

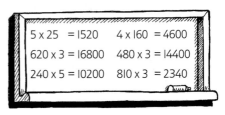

$5 \times 25 = 1520$ $4 \times 160 = 4600$

$620 \times 3 = 16800$ $480 \times 3 = 14400$

$240 \times 5 = 10200$ $810 \times 3 = 2340$

Point to a multiplication, and
choose several children to say why it is incorrect, and what the correct
answer should be. Repeat for each multiplication.

Target number

Multiplying, adding and subtracting
Write a target number on the board, e.g. 1202.
Each pair works to find a way of making the target by multiplying
(a 1-digit number by a multiple of 100), then adding or subtracting
(e.g. $400 \times 3 = 1200$, $1200 + 2 = 1202$).
Ask different pairs for their solutions. Discuss the different ways.
Repeat for a new target.

Bingo

Addition bonds to 100
Number cards (1 to 100)
Each pair writes five bingo numbers (0 to 100).
Select a card at random, hold it up and read it
aloud. Choose a child to say the addition bond to 100. Any pair with a
matching number can cross it out.

75	25	17
	42 35	83

Twenty questions

Place-value, adding, subtracting, doubling, multiplying, halving
Read out these numbered questions, writing them on the board as you
read them. Allow about 30 seconds for children to write the answer to
each, before moving on to the next question.

1. Write this number: fifty-one thousand and twenty.
2. What is 2 less than 20 000?
3. $31 \times 4 =$
4. $24 \times 5 =$
5. $3.5 \times 3 =$
6. $12.5 - 1.5 =$
7. $12.5 - 1.6 =$
8. $1536 - 636 =$
9. $430 - 199 =$
10. $72 - 65 =$
11. $164 - 148 = ? - 150$
12. $3.2 - 1.9 =$
13. double 87
14. $52 + 53 + 54 + 55 =$
15. $\frac{2}{7}$ of 28
16. Write three hundredths as a decimal.
17. 25% of 5000 =
18. $4 \times 28 =$
19. $35 \times 3 =$
20. Round 3.45 to the nearest whole number.

Number of the week

Sample tasks
- Multiply 20, 30, 40, 50, ... by our number.
- Multiply 100, 200, 300, ... by our number.
- Multiply 21, 41, 31, 51, ... by our number.

Sample facts
- it is a square number (2×2)
- it is the number of sides of a quadrilateral
- it is a factor of 16, of 44 and of 28

Word of the week

Sample tasks
- How many **decades** in 100 years? 100 years is 10 **decades**.
- How many **decades** do you hope to live? I hope to live 8 **decades**.
- How many **decades** have your mother/father/grandmother lived? My grandmother has lived for 5 **decades**.

Sample facts
- a **decade** is a period of 10 years
- a **decade** is one tenth of a century
- 1 year is a tenth of a **decade**

Shape of the week

Sample facts
- a parallelogram is a type of quadrilateral
- a parallelogram has two pairs of opposite parallel sides
- a parallelogram has two pairs of equal sides and two pairs of equal angles
- a parallelogram with all four sides equal is called a rhombus
- a parallelogram is not symmetrical

N15 Multiplication

Show me

Multiplying a decimal (hundredths) by 10
Number cards (0 to 9), one set per pair
Set the children tasks where they have to match a particular criterion
using the cards. For example:
Show me 0.34, 0.56, 0.12, ... multiplied by 10
Show me 1.15, 1.57, 2.4, ... multiplied by 10.

Table timer

Multiplying by 20, 50 and 100
Draw a table with four columns. In the first
column write numbers up to 100 at random.
Children copy the table, multiplying by 20
and writing the answer in the second column,
by 100 in the third column and by 50 in the
fourth column.
Time them.

	x 20	x 100	x 50
4			
28			
30			

Missing numbers

*Multiplying a 3-digit by a 1-digit
number*
Write ten multiplications on the
board, of a 3-digit by a 1-digit
number. In each case replace
some of the digits with a '?'.
Point to a missing digit and

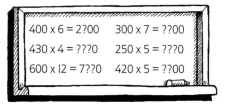

400 x 6 = 2?00   300 x 7 = ??00
430 x 4 = ???0   250 x 5 = ???0
600 x 12 = 7??0   420 x 5 = ??00

choose a child to say what it is. Repeat for each missing digit.

Open the box

Dividing a 2-digit by a 1-digit number
Draw a 2 × 5 grid on the board. Cover each space with a division of a
2-digit number by 2, 3, 4 or 5. Underneath write the answer.
Choose a child to point to a box and say the answer (they can work on
the board to help). Check with the class.
The child can 'open the box', to reveal the answer.

Bingo

Subtracting 99 from a 3-digit number

Number cards (0 to 9)

Each pair writes five 3-digit bingo numbers.
Select three cards at random. Make a 3-digit number, hold it up and read it aloud.
Choose a child to subtract 99 and say the answer.
The winners are the first pair to cross out two of their numbers.

Number of the week

Sample tasks
- Multiply 80, 20, 60, 120, by our number.
- Divide 50, 200, 350, 600, ... by our number.
- Multiply our number by 3, 9, 12, 20, 50, ...
- Are these numbers divisible by our number: 340, 215, 784, 168, 530, 95, ...?

Sample facts
- it is a prime number
- it is a factor of any 2-digit number which has a units digit of 0 or 5
- it is the number of sides of a pentagon

Word of the week

Sample tasks
- What is the **mean** of 2 and 8? The **mean** of 2 and 8 is 5.
- How do you find the **mean** of 3 heights? To find the **mean** you find the total of all three, then divide by 3.
- If the **mean** of 2 numbers is 10, and one of them is 14, What is the other? If the **mean** is 10, the other is 6.

Sample facts
- a **mean** is a type of average
- to find the **mean** of a set of numbers, add them together, then divide the total by the number in the set
- the **mean** of 2 and 3 is 2·5 (2 + 3 = 5 ÷ 2 = 2·5)

N16 Fractions

Grid fractions

Finding quarters

Draw a 2 × 5 grid on the board, with a 3-digit multiple of 4 in each space.
Children copy the grid, finding one quarter of each number.
When the grid is complete, point to each space in turn, asking a different child to say their answer.

All wrong

Equivalent fractions
Write ten mixed fractions on the board, and their equivalents.
Ensure that they are all incorrect.
Point to an equation, and choose several children to say

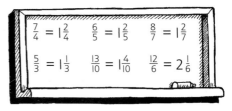

$$\frac{7}{4} = 1\frac{2}{4} \qquad \frac{6}{5} = 1\frac{2}{5} \qquad \frac{8}{7} = 1\frac{2}{7}$$

$$\frac{5}{3} = 1\frac{1}{3} \qquad \frac{13}{10} = 1\frac{4}{10} \qquad \frac{12}{6} = 2\frac{1}{6}$$

why it is incorrect, and what the correct answer should be.
Repeat for each equation.

Make me

Adding and multiplying
Write 6, 12, 110, 200 on the board, each in a triangle.
Write 14 510, 132 012, 3060, 2520 on the board, each in a circle.
The children can combine any or all of the triangle numbers by adding or multiplying.
Can they make any of the circle numbers?
Allow ten minutes. Discuss the different answers.

Codes

Finding halves
Number cards (0 to 9) one set per pair
Write these coded equations on the board:

$\frac{1}{2}$ of e = $\frac{1}{2}$ $\frac{1}{2}$ of n = e $\frac{1}{2}$ of en = d $\frac{1}{2}$ of d = g

$\frac{1}{4}$ of k = n $\frac{1}{2}$ of l is n $\frac{1}{2}$ of eo = a $\frac{1}{2}$ of el = u

$\frac{1}{2}$ of yo = la $\frac{1}{2}$ of k = l $\frac{1}{2}$ of up = ga

Each digit (0 to 9) is represented by one letter only.
0 is represented by o. Allow the children five minutes to explore the code. Discuss the solution.

Twenty questions

Place-value, adding, subtracting, doubling, multiplying, halving
Read out these numbered questions, writing them on the board as you
read them. Allow about 30 seconds for children to write the answer to
each, before moving on to the next question.

1 Write this number: one hundred and six thousand and six.

2 $30\,002 - 3 =$ **3** $7 \times 25 =$ **4** $7 \times 28 =$

5 $540 + 460 =$ **6** $2.7 + 6.3 =$ **7** $4.5 + ? = 10$

8 $3.2 + ? = 10$ **9** $5.9 + 3.4 =$ **10** $6.3 - 1.9 =$

11 $\frac{1}{3}$ of $210 =$ **12** $4 \times 7 =$ **13** $8 \times 7 =$

14 $7 \times 12 =$ **15** $7 \times 120 =$ **16** $2.5 + 2.6 =$

17 $7.5 + 7.6 =$ **18** $4.25 + ? = 5$ **19** double 3.45

20 What is two hundredths less than 3.4?

Number of the week	**Sample tasks**	**Sample facts**
	• What is half of our number? • What is double our number? • How many quarters are in our number? Write it ($\frac{9}{4}$).	• there are 135 minutes in $2\frac{1}{4}$ hours • $2\frac{1}{4}$ right-angles are $180 + 22\frac{1}{2}$ degrees $= 202\frac{1}{2}$ degrees

---

Word of the week

Sample tasks
• Is 60° an acute angle? Yes it is an **acute angle**.
• How many **acute angles** can a triangle have? A triangle can have 2 or 3 **acute angles**.
• How many minutes can pass when the minute hand of a clock turns through an **acute angle**? When turning through an **acute angle** it must be less than 15 minutes.

Sample facts
• an **acute angle** is an angle less than 1 right angle
• it is impossible for a triangle to have only 1 **acute angle**
• half a right angle is an **acute angle**

Shape of the week

Sample facts
• an arc is a part of the boundary of a circle
• the length of the arc of a quarter-circle is one quarter of the circumference of the circle
• an arc is part of a sector of a circle
• a semi-circular arc is half of a circle
• the length of an arc is longer than the distance between the two ends of the arc

N17 Fractions

Table timer

Multiplying by 2, 4 and 8
Draw a table with four columns. In the first
column write 3-digit numbers at random.
Children copy the table, multiplying by 2 and
writing the answer in the second column, by 4
in the third column and by 8 in the fourth
column. Point out that they can double across
each row to find the answers.
Time them.

	x 2	x 4	x 8
120			
260			
300			

Show me

Dividing a multiple of 100 by a 1- or 2-digit number
Number cards (0 to 9), two sets per pair
Set the children tasks where they have to match a particular criterion
using the cards. for example:
Show me 100 divided by 2, 5, 10
Show me 200 divided by 5, 20, 10
Show me 500 divided by 10, 5, 50.

Missing numbers

Equivalent fractions
Write ten fractions on the board
and an equivalent to each. In each
case replace one of the numbers
with a '?'.
Point to a missing number and
choose a child to say what it is.
Repeat for each missing number.

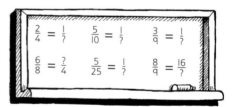

$$\frac{2}{4} = \frac{1}{?} \qquad \frac{5}{10} = \frac{1}{?} \qquad \frac{3}{9} = \frac{1}{?}$$

$$\frac{6}{8} = \frac{?}{4} \qquad \frac{5}{25} = \frac{1}{?} \qquad \frac{8}{9} = \frac{16}{?}$$

Bingo

Equivalent fractions
Number cards (2, 4, 6, 8, 10)
Each pair writes five bingo numbers that are simple fractions
($\frac{1}{2}$, $\frac{1}{3}$, $\frac{3}{4}$ etc.).
Select two cards at random. Make a fraction, hold it up and read
it aloud. Choose a child to say the fraction in its simplest form (if it can
be simplified). Any pair with a matching fraction can cross it out.

Grid fractions

Equivalent fractions
Draw a 2 × 5 grid on the board, with a fraction in each space.
Children copy the grid, writing an equivalent fraction each time.
When the grid is complete, point to each space in turn, asking a
different child to say their answer.

Number of the week

Sample tasks
- How many sixths, ninths, ... match our number?
- What must be added to our number to make 3 wholes?
- What is half of our number?

Sample facts
- $\frac{2}{3}$ of an hour is 40 minutes
- $\frac{2}{3}$ of a right-angle is 60 degrees
- $\frac{2}{3}$ of 15 is 10, $\frac{2}{3}$ of 300 is 200, $\frac{2}{3}$ of 18 is 12

Word of the week

Sample tasks
- Draw two straight lines which **intersect**. These lines **intersect**.
- Draw a pair of parallel lines, and another line which **intersects** them both. Here is the **intersecting** line.
- Show me two roads on this map which **intersect**. Here is the **intersection** of these two roads.

Sample facts
- when two lines **intersect** the opposite angles are equal
- parallel lines do not **intersect**
- the sides of a triangle **intersect** at the vertices

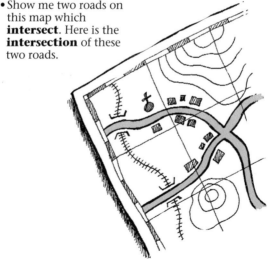

N18 Percentages

Grid percentages

Finding percentages
Draw a 2×5 grid on the board, with a 2-digit number in each space (mostly multiples of 10).
Children copy the grid, finding that percentage of 400 each time.
When the grid is complete, point to each space in turn, asking a different child to say their answer.
Repeat for a different amount, e.g. 300, 500.

All wrong

Fractions, decimals and percentages
Write ten percentages on the board, and their fraction or decimal equivalents. Ensure that they are all incorrect.
Point to an equation, and choose several children to say why it is incorrect, and what the correct answer should be. Repeat for each equation.

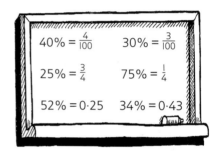

$$40\% = \tfrac{4}{100} \qquad 30\% = \tfrac{3}{100}$$
$$25\% = \tfrac{3}{4} \qquad 75\% = \tfrac{1}{4}$$
$$52\% = 0\cdot25 \qquad 34\% = 0\cdot43$$

Target number

Doubling, adding and subtracting
Write a target number on the board, e.g. 123.
Each pair works to find a way of making the target by doubling, then adding or subtracting (e.g. double 48 = 96, 96 + 27 = 123).
Ask different pairs for their solutions. Discuss the different ways.
Repeat for a new target.

Open the box

Decimal fractions
Draw a 2×5 grid on the board.
Cover each space with a fraction (tenths or hundredths),

$0\cdot32$	$1\cdot02$	$\tfrac{16}{100}$	$1\tfrac{3}{10}$	$\tfrac{2}{100}$
$4\tfrac{4}{100}$	$\tfrac{52}{100}$	$1\tfrac{13}{100}$	$\tfrac{1}{10}$	$6\tfrac{1}{100}$

and underneath write the matching decimal.
Choose a child to point to a box and write the matching decimal on the board. Check with the class.
The child can 'open the box', to reveal the answer.

Twenty questions

Place-value, adding, subtracting, doubling, multiplying, halving

Read out these numbered questions, writing them on the board as you read them. Allow about 30 seconds for children to write the answer to each, before moving on to the next question.

1 Write this number: one hundred and sixty-four thousand, and fifty-four.

2 What is three tenths less than 4.25?

3 $3.8 - 1.7 =$

4 $3.8 - 1.9 =$

5 $4.3 - 3.8 =$

6 $29 + 29 + 29 =$

7 $1.9 + 1.9 + 1.9 =$

8 $\frac{5}{?} = \frac{1}{2}$

9 $\frac{14}{5} = \frac{??}{5}$

10 $8 \times 20 =$

11 $8 \times 202 =$

12 $208 + 298 =$

13 $450 + 451 =$

14 $280 + 720 =$

15 $55 \times 3 =$

16 $4735 - 3735 =$

17 $\frac{3}{4}$ of $48 =$

18 $\frac{2}{5}$ of $100 =$

19 15% of $300 =$

20 $4.2 + ? = 5$

Number of the week

Sample tasks
- How many hundredths is our number?
- What is our number as a decimal and as a fraction?
- Are these more or less than our number: $\frac{3}{10}$, 0.15, $\frac{2}{5}$, 0.4, ...?

Sample facts
- 20% of a whole is one fifth of a whole
- if 20% of an item is coloured, then 80% is not
- 20% of £1 is 20p

Word of the week

Sample tasks
- Draw a **hexagonal** shape. This shape is **hexagonal**.
- Is this **hexagonal**? No, it is not **hexagonal**, it has 7 sides.
- Sort these shapes into **hexagonal** and **non-hexagonal**.

Sample facts
- a **hexagonal** shape is shaped like a hexagon
- **hexagonal** shapes have two less sides than octagonal shapes
- a honeycomb creates a **hexagonal** pattern

Shape of the week

Sample facts
- a hexagonal prism is a prism whose 'end-pieces' (cross section) are hexagons
- a hexagonal prism has 8 faces: 2 hexagons and 6 rectangles
- a hexagonal prism has 12 vertices
- a hexagonal prism has 18 edges: 6 each at the two ends, and 6 across the prism

(N19) Percentages

Table timer

Multiplying by 3, 6 and 12
Draw a table with four columns. In the first
column write numbers up to 20 at random.
Children copy the table, multiplying by 3 and
writing the answer in the second column, by 6
in the third column and by 12 in the fourth
column. Point out that they can double across
each row to find the answers.
Time them.

	x 3	x 6	x 12
10			
16			
5			

Show me

Finding percentages
Number cards (0 to 9), two sets per pair
Set the children tasks where they have to match a particular criterion
using the cards. For example:
Show me 10% of 100, 200, 250, 320, 180
Show me 25% of 100, 200, 80, 120
Show me 30% of 100, 900, 300
Show me 15% of 100, 200, 800.

Missing numbers

Finding percentages
Write ten equations on the
board – finding a percentage of
a multiple of 10. In each case
replace one or more of the digits
with a '?'. Point to a missing
digit and choose a child to say what it is.
Repeat for each missing digit.

> 50% of 160 = ?0   25% of 360 = ?0
> 24% of 400 = ??   48% of 1000 = ??0
> 45% of 500 = ??5   12% of 500 = ?0

Bingo

Finding 10%
Number cards (10 to 100)
Each pair writes five 2-digit bingo numbers.
Select a card at random (hidden from the class), multiply by 10 and
write it on the board, e.g. 480.
Choose a child to find 10% of the number and say the answer, i.e. 48%.
Any pair with a matching number can cross it out.

Codes

Finding percentages

Number cards (0 to 9), one set per pair

Write these coded equations on the board:

mo% of to = t	mo% of co = c	mo% of ho = h
so% of aoo = mco	ao% of eo = ma	ao% of ao = c
no% of ro = as	ch% of coo = mto	ho% of aoo = moo

Each digit (0 to 9) is represented by one letter only.

0 is represented by o.

Allow the children five minutes to explore the code.

Discuss the solution.

Number of the week

Sample tasks
- What is 10% of £2, £5, £40, £15, ...?
- What is the price at 10% discount on £20, £30, £200, £25, ...?
- What is the price at 10% increase on £20, £30, £200, £25, ...?

Sample facts
- 10% is the same as one tenth
- 10% discount on a price means that it cost 90% of the price
- 10% of £24 is £2.40 and 10% of 1 centimetre is 1 millimetre

---

Word of the week

obtuse angle

Sample tasks
- Is 160° an **obtuse angle**? Yes it is an **obtuse angle**.
- Draw an **obtuse angle**. this is an **obtuse angle**.
- An **obtuse angle** for the hands of a clock must be between 15 and 30 minutes.

Sample facts
- an **obtuse angle** is an angle between 1 and 2 right-angles
- it is impossible for a triangle to have 2 **obtuse angles**
- one and a half right angles is an **obtuse angle**

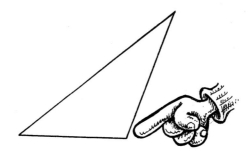

N20 Multiples

Grid multiplication

Multiplying a 2-digit by a 1-digit number
Draw a 2 × 5 grid on the board, with a 2-digit number in each space.
Children copy the grid, multiplying each number by 6.
When the grid is complete, point to each space in turn, asking a
different child to say their answer.
Repeat for multiplying by 9, 8, 5, ...

All wrong

*Multiplying a 3-digit multiple of
10 by a 1-digit number*
Write ten multiplications of a
3-digit multiple of 10 by a
1-digit number on the board.
Ensure that they are all

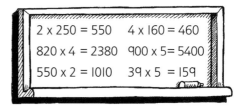

incorrect. Point to a multiplication, and choose several children to say
why it is incorrect, and what the correct answer should be.
Repeat for each multiplication.

Make me

Adding and multiplying
Write 2, 240, 3, 360, 5 on the board, each in a triangle.
Write 1565, 3480, 11 040, 7200 on the board, each in a circle.
The children can combine any or all of the triangle numbers by adding
or multiplying. Can they make any of the circle numbers?
Allow ten minutes. Discuss the different answers.

Open the box

Multiplying by 200, 300 and 400
Draw a 2 × 5 grid on the board. Cover each space with a multiplication
of a 1-digit number by 200, 300 or 400. Underneath write the answer.
Choose a child to point to a box and say the answer.
Check with the class. The child can 'open the box', to reveal the answer.

Twenty questions

Place-value, adding, subtracting, doubling, multiplying, halving
Read out these numbered questions, writing them on the board as you
read them. Allow about 30 seconds for children to write the answer to
each, before moving on to the next question.

1 Write this number: one hundred and six thousand and six.
2 What is 3 more than 10 998?   3 $450 \times 2 =$ 4 $480 \times 2 =$
5 $660 \div 3 =$ 6 $2.7 + ? = 3$ 7 $27 + ? = 100$
8 $270 + ? = 1000$ 9 $3.8 + 2.2 =$ 10 $345 - 199 =$
11 $164 - 156 =$ 12 $321 - 158 = ? - 160$ 13 $3.81 - 0.03 =$
14 $91 + 91 + 93 =$ 15 $35 \times 4 =$ 16 $7 \times 8 =$
17 $6 \times 9 =$ 18 $8 \times 30 =$ 19 1, 3, 6, 10, ‿ ‿
20 Write one hundredth as a decimal.

Number of the week

Sample tasks
• Say the multiples of 2 (then of 3, of 4, ...).
• Say a common multiple of 2 and of 3, of 2 and of 5, of 2 and of 7, ...
• Say the second multiple of 15, of 13, of 27, ...

Sample facts
• it is the only even prime number
• it is the number in a pair
• it is a factor of all even numbers

Word of the week

speed

Sample tasks
• What does this road sign showing '30' mean? You must not travel at a **speed** of more than 30 miles per hour.
• What is your average **speed** if you travel 40 miles in 2 hours? My average **speed** is 20 miles per hour.
• If you travel at a **speed** of 30 miles per hour for 3 hours, how far have you

travelled? At that average **speed** I will travel 90 miles.

Sample facts
• **speed** can be measured in miles per hour or kilometres per hour
• a speedometer on a car is an instrument which measures **speed**
• 10 miles per hour is a faster **speed** than 10 kilometres per hour

---

Shape of the week

rhombus

Sample facts
• a rhombus is a parallelogram with all four sides equal
• a rhombus is a 'squashed' square
• a rhombus is symmetrical
• a rhombus has opposite equal angles
• the diagonals of a rhombus are perpendicular to each other

N21 Square numbers

Table timer

Multiplying by 5, 10 and 20
Draw a table with four columns. In the first
column write 2-digit numbers at random.
Children copy the table, multiplying by 5 and
writing the answer in the second column, by
10 in the third column and by 20 in the fourth
column. Time them.

	x 5	x 10	x 20
15			
41			
63			

Bingo

Square numbers
Number cards (0 to 12)
Each pair writes five bingo numbers that are square numbers up to 144.
Select a card at random, hold it up and read it aloud.
Choose a child to multiply the number by itself.
Any pair with a matching number can cross it out.

Missing numbers

Squaring multiples of 10
Write ten multiplications on the
board, of a number multiplied
by itself. In each case replace
one or more of the numbers
with a '?'.

$30 \times 30 = ?$ $? \times ? = 10,000$

$80 \times 80 = ?$ $11 \times 11 = ?$

$? \times ? = 8100$ $? \times ? = 400$

Point to a missing number and choose a child to say what it is.
Repeat for each missing number.

Three in a row

Subtracting one 2-digit number from another by counting on
**Four small number grids (1 to 100), counters, large number grid
(1 to 100)**
Divide the class into four teams, and give each team a number grid and
some counters.
Point to two 2-digit numbers on the large grid (within ten places of each
other, e.g. 38 and 46). Choose a child to say the difference between the
two numbers. If the child answers correctly the team can cover either of
the two numbers on their grid with a counter.
Continue, choosing a child from each team in turn.
The winner is the first team to place three counters in any row
or column.

Codes

Adding two 3-digit numbers

Number cards (0 to 9), one set per pair

Write these coded additions on the board:

mth + m = mts   msw + mm = mwx   moo + moo = aoo

zzz + m = mooo   txy + waa = mooo   sht + hsx = mooo

Each digit (0 to 9) is represented by one letter only. 0 is represented by o.
Allow the children five minutes to explore the code.
Discuss the solution.

Number of the week

16

Sample tasks

- Say the square number before and after our number.
- What is the square root of our number?
- Continue halving from our number: 16, 8, 4, 2, 1, $\frac{1}{2}$, ...

Sample facts

- it is the fourth square number
- it is 10% of 160
- It has an odd number of factors, i.e. 5 factors: 1, 2, 4, 8, 16

Word of the week

median

Sample tasks

- What is the **median** of: 2, 3, 5, 7, 9? The **median** is 5.
- What is the **median** of: 7, 9, 8, 5,? The data in order is: 5, 7, 8, 9, which has two middle numbers: 7, 8. The **median** is the mean of these: 7.5.
- For the data: 3, 4, 5, which is the larger: the mean or **median**? The mean and **median** are the same, both 4.

Sample facts

- the **median** is the middle observation in a set of data, when written in order from smallest to largest
- the **median** and mean are both types of average
- the **median** of an even set of observations is the mean of the two middle numbers

N22 Factors

All wrong

Dividing a 2-digit by a 1-digit number
Write ten divisions on the board, of a 2-digit by a 1-digit number. Ensure that they are all incorrect. Point to a division, and choose

$42 \div 6 = 8$	$64 \div 8 = 9$
$72 \div 9 = 9$	$65 \div 5 = 12$
$36 \div 4 = 10$	$45 \div 9 = 6$

several children to say why it is incorrect, and what the correct answer should be. Repeat for each division.

Grid factors

Finding factors
Draw a 2 × 5 grid on the board, with a 2-digit number in each space. Children copy the grid, writing the factors of each number. When the grid is complete, point to each space in turn, asking a different child to say their answer.

Target number

Dividing, adding and subtracting
Write a target number on the board, e.g. 4. Each pair works to find a way of making the target by dividing (a 2-digit number by a 1-digit number), then adding or subtracting.
Ask different pairs for their solutions. Discuss the different ways. Repeat for a new target.

$$4$$
$$72 \div 9 = 8$$
$$8 - 4 = 4$$

Show me

Adding several 1- and 2-digit numbers
Number cards (0 to 9), one set per pair
Set the children tasks where they have to match a particular criterion using the cards. For example:
Show me 50 + 20 + 3, 60 + 30 + 4, 20 + 10 + 18
Show me 55 + 31, 28 + 23, 54 + 29
Show me 4 + 5 + 6, 9 + 4 + 10, 3 + 8 + 7.

Twenty questions

Place-value, adding, subtracting, doubling, multiplying, halving
Read out these numbered questions, writing them on the board as you read them.

Allow about 30 seconds for children to write the answer to each, before moving on to the next question.

1 Write this number: one hundred thousand and ten.

2 What is 6 less than 10 005? **3** 4400 ÷ 4 = **4** 6 × 22 =

5 6.1 − 0.9 = **6** 5.5 − 3.6 = **7** 64 − 32 =

8 86 − 44 = **9** 297 + 311 = **10** 38 − 29 =

11 134 − 56 = **12** 1967 + 2243 is approximately...

13 254 + 253 + 252 = **14** double 67 **15** double 135

16 halve 670 **17** 20 × 21 **18** 3 × 6 × 5

19 How many eights in 640? **20** 2 × 4 × 7 × 10

Number of the week

Sample tasks
- Say the prime numbers counting back from our number.
- Say the next 5 prime numbers on from our number.
- Say the multiples of our number: 23, 46, 69, ...

Sample facts
- it is a prime number – has exactly 2 factors
- its digits are consecutive
- it nearest square number is 25

Word of the week

Sample tasks
- Look at a local map. Draw a circle with the school at the centre, radius 1 **mile**. Which places are exactly 1 **mile** from school?
- Is the football ground more or less than 1 **mile** from school? it is more than 1 **mile** away.
- Find out how many **miles** it is to London and to Manchester. it is 180 **miles** to London, and 40 **miles** to Manchester.

Sample facts
- a **mile** is longer than a kilometre
- a **mile** is an Imperial unit for measuring distance
- a marathon run is a distance of just more than 26 **miles**

Shape of the week

Sample facts
- an isosceles triangle has two of its three sides equal
- an isosceles triangle has two of its three angles equal – these are sometimes called 'base angles'
- a right-angled isosceles triangle has two angles of 45°
- a square can be divided into two right-angled isosceles triangles
- some parts of roofs are shaped like an isosceles triangle

 Division

Table timer

Multiplying by 3, 6 and 12

Draw a table with four columns. In the first column write numbers up to 12 at random. Children copy the table, multiplying by 3 and writing the answer in the second column, by 6 in the third column and by 12 in the fourth column. Point out that they can double across each row to find the answers. Time them.

	x 3	x 6	x 12
4			
10			
12			

Bingo

Divisibility rules

Number cards (0 to 9)

Each pair writes five bingo numbers (2, 3, 4, 5, 6, 9, 10).

Select three cards at random. Make a 3-digit number, hold it up and read it aloud. Choose a child to decide if the number divides by any of 2, 3, 4, 5, 6, 9 or 10, using a divisibility rule.

Any pair with a matching number can cross it out – they can cross out only one number in each round.

Missing numbers

Divisibility rules

Write ten 3-digit numbers on the board. In brackets after each list the numbers (2 to 9) that will divide equally into that number. In each case replace one or more of the numbers with a '?'.

Point to a missing number and choose a child to say what it is.

Repeat for each missing number.

285 (?, ?), 639 (?, ?), 724 (?), 159 (?), 354 (?), 288 (?, ?, ?, ?), 765 (?, ?, ?), 366 (?, ?), 525 (?, ?), 903 (?),

Open the box

Dividing by 2, 3 and 4

Draw a 2 × 5 grid on the board. Cover each space with a division of a 2-digit number by 2, 3 or 4. Underneath write the answer.

22	13	24÷3	64÷2	81÷3
44÷4	33÷3	84÷4	60÷2	92÷4

Choose a child to point to a box and say the answer (they can work on the board to help). Check with the class.

The child can 'open the box', to reveal the answer.

Codes

Divisibility rules

Number cards (0 to 9), one set per pair

Write these clues on the board:

ite divides by 3 and 5

und divides by 2 and 9

net divides by 2 and 4 but not by 3

aee divides by 5 and by 9

ato divides by 4 and 6 and 5

cnr divides by 3 and 9 but not by 2

ccu divides by 3 only

Each digit (0 to 9) is represented by one letter only.

0 is represented by o.

Allow the children five minutes to explore the code.

Discuss the solution.

Number of the week

Sample tasks

- Can these numbers be divided by our number: 21, 71, 35, 42, 163, ...?
- Multiply these numbers by our number; 5, 7, 3, 9, 15, 20, 400, ...
- Divide these numbers by our number: 300, 150, 900, 6000, 69, ...

Sample facts

- it is a prime number
- it is a factor of 27, of 30, of 21 and of 96
- it will divide exactly into any number whose digit total is a multiple of our number

---

Word of the week

Sample tasks

- Approximately how many grams is 1 **ounce**? 1 **ounce** is approximately 25 grams.
- Approximately how many **ounces** is 200 grams? 200 grams is approximately 8 **ounces**.
- Weight this object in grams, then approximate its weight in **ounces**. Its weight is about half a kilogram, which is about 18 **ounces**.

Sample facts

- an **ounce** is an Imperial unit for measuring weight (mass)
- 4 **ounces** is about 100 grams
- 16 **ounces** is the same weight as 1 pound

N24 Equations

Grid division

Dividing a 2-digit by a 1-digit number
Draw a 2 × 5 grid on the board, with a 2-digit multiple of 3 in each
space. Children copy the grid, dividing each number by 3.
When the grid is complete, point to each space in turn, asking a
different child to say their answer. Repeat for dividing by 4, 5, 6 ...

Make me

Adding, subtracting, dividing
Write 432, 9, 810, 5 on the board, each in a triangle.
Write 200, 450, 24 on the board, each in a circle.
The children can combine any or all of the triangle numbers by adding,
subtracting or dividing. Can they make any of the circle numbers?
Allow ten minutes. Discuss the different answers.

Missing numbers

Equations
Write ten equations on the
board, a mixture of addition,
subtraction, multiplication and
division. In each case replace
one of the numbers with a '?'.
Point to a missing number and

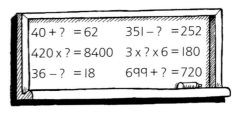

$40 + ? = 62$ $351 - ? = 252$
$420 \times ? = 8400$ $3 \times ? \times 6 = 180$
$36 - ? = 18$ $699 + ? = 720$

choose a child to say what it is. Repeat for each missing number.

Three in a row

Estimating the division of a 3-digit by a 2-digit number
Four small number grids (1 to 100), counters
Divide the class into four teams, and give each team a number grid and
some counters. Write a division of a 3-digit by a 2-digit number, e.g. 382
÷ 19 on the board. Choose a child to estimate the answer. Check with
the class. If the child makes a good estimate the team can cover that
number on their grid with a counter. Continue, choosing a child from
each team in turn. The winners are the first to place three counters in
any row or column.

Twenty questions

Place-value, adding, subtracting, doubling, multiplying, halving
Read out these numbered questions, writing them on the board as you
read them. Allow about 30 seconds for children to write the answer to
each, before moving on to the next question.

1 What number is four more than 65 998?

2 double 3.6

3 Does 456 divide by 3?   **4** 120 ÷ 4 =

5 18 + ? = 24

6 29 × 2 =   **7** 299 × 2 =

8 4.2 + ? =

9 Round 2.49 to the nearest whole number.

10 560 + ? = 1000

11 $\frac{2}{3}$ of 33 =   **12** 565 – 466 =

13 43 + 44 + 45 =

14 208 – 189 =   **15** 32 × 4 =

16 400 × 40 =

17 43 – 24 =   **18** 5% of 200 =

19 3.4 + 3.8 =

20 Round 2856 to the nearest hundred.

Number of the week

Sample tasks
- What must be added to our number to make 10, 18, 29, ...?
- What must be subtracted from our number to leave 1, 6, 3, ...?
- What must we subtract from 15, 23, 9, 56, ... to leave our number?

Sample facts
- it is the fourth prime number and the fourth odd number
- it is the number of days in a week, the number of sides of a heptagon
- it is the square root of 49

Word of the week

Sample tasks
- If you buy for 5p and sell for 7p have you made a **profit** or a loss? I have made a **profit** of 2p.
- If you buy something for 10p, then sell it for 15p, what is your **profit**? The **profit** is 5p.
- If you buy something for £1, what do you have to sell it for to make a **profit** of 20p?

Sample facts
- **profit** is the amount of money gained from buying and then selling something
- a **profit** of 100% is made when selling something for double the cost
- **profit** is the opposite to loss

Shape of the week

Sample facts
- a scalene triangle is a triangle whose sides are all of different lengths
- if a triangles angles are all different, then the triangle is scalene
- isosceles and equilateral triangles are not scalene
- a right-angled triangle can be a scalene triangle
- scalene triangles tessellate

N25 Subtraction

Table timer

Addition bonds to 100 and 1000
Draw two tables with two columns. In the first table write 2-digit numbers at random in the first column. In the second table write 3-digit multiples of 10 at random in the first column. Children copy the table, writing

	Make 100
41	
13	
88	

	Make 1000
210	
400	
660	

the addition bond to 100, and the addition bond to 1000 in the correct table. Time them.

All wrong

Subtracting a 1-digit from a 2-digit number
Write ten subtractions on the board – a 1-digit from a 2-digit number. Ensure that they are all incorrect. Point to a subtraction, and choose several children to

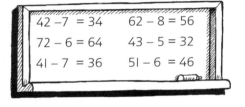

$42 - 7 = 34$ $62 - 8 = 56$
$72 - 6 = 64$ $43 - 5 = 32$
$41 - 7 = 36$ $51 - 6 = 46$

say why it is incorrect, and what the correct answer should be.
Repeat for each subtraction.

Target number

Doubling and subtracting
Write a target number on the board, e.g. 86.
Each pair works to find a way of making the target by doubling any number then subtracting a number less than 20 (e.g. double 45 = 90, 90 – 4 = 86). Ask different pairs for their solutions. Discuss the different ways. Repeat for a new target.

Bingo

Rounding a 4-digit number to the nearest thousand
Two sets of number cards (0 to 9)
Each pair writes five bingo numbers that are multiples of 1000.
Select four cards at random (use both sets). Make a 4-digit number, hold it up and read it aloud.
Choose a child to round to the nearest thousand.
Any pair with a matching number can cross it out.

Codes

Adding to make multiples of 1000

Number cards (0 to 9) one set per pair

Write these coded additions on the board:

tnoo + noo = 2000	taoo + uoo = 2000	tyyy + t = 2000
tnnn + iin = 2000	trrr + uus = 2000	riau + nba = 3000
niyy + inot = 10 000	taby + bat = 2000	trai + ubb = 2000

Each digit (0 to 9) is represented by one letter only.

0 is represented by o.

Allow the children five minutes to explore the code.

Discuss the solution.

Number of the week (3571)	**Sample tasks** • Read our number, then 1 more, then 1 less. Read 10 more, then 10 less. • Round our number to its nearest 10, nearest 100, nearest 1000. • Read the number with its digits reversed.	**Sample facts** • it is between 3000 and 4000, between 3500 and 3600, between 3570 and 3580 • it is 429 less than 4000 • its digit total is a square number

---

Word of the week **product**	**Sample tasks** • What is the **product** of 5 and 7? The **product** of 5 and 7 is 35. • If the **product** of two numbers is 24, what are the numbers? For a **product** of 24, the two numbers could be: 1 and 24, 2 and 12, 3 and 8, 4 and 6. • What is the **product** of 2, 3 and 5. The **product** of 2, 3 and 5 is 30.	**Sample facts** • when numbers are multiplied together, the answer is called the **product** • 7 and 8 have a **product** of 56 – 7 and 8 are factors of 56 • the **product** of a number and itself is a square number

N26 Division

Grid division

Dividing a 2- or 3-digit number by a 1-digit number (with remainders)
Draw a 2 × 5 grid on the board, with a 2- or 3-digit number in
each space.
Children copy the grid, dividing each number by 5, and writing the
answer and any remainder.
When the grid is complete, point to each space in turn, asking a
different child to say their answer.
Repeat for dividing by 4, 6, 7, ...

Missing numbers

Addition bonds to 1000
Write ten additions on the board
– 3-digit multiples of 10 to 1000.
In each case replace one of the
numbers with a '?'.
Point to a missing number and
choose a child to say what it is.
Repeat for each missing number.

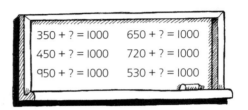

350 + ? = 1000   650 + ? = 1000
450 + ? = 1000   720 + ? = 1000
950 + ? = 1000   530 + ? = 1000

Make me

Adding and multiplying
Write 350, 4, 35, 5, 30 on the board, each in a triangle.
Write 14 000, 640, 1470, 540, 695 on the board, each in a circle.
The children can combine any or all of the triangle numbers by adding
or multiplying.
Can they make any of the circle numbers? Allow ten minutes.
Discuss the different answers.

Open the box

*Dividing a 2- or 3-digit number by
a 1-digit number (with remainders)*
Draw a 2 × 5 grid on the board.
Cover each space with a division

| 4 r3 | 2 r1 | 49÷4 | 132÷5 | 43÷3 |
| 22÷4 | 456÷5 | 88÷3 | 61÷2 | 33÷2 |

of a 2- or 3-digit number by 2, 3, 4 or 5 (with a remainder). Underneath
write the answer and the remainder.
Choose a child to point to a box and say the answer (they can work on
the board to help). Check with the class.
The child can 'open the box', to reveal the answer and the remainder.

Twenty questions

Place-value, adding, subtracting, doubling, multiplying, halving

Read out these numbered questions, writing them on the board as you read them. Allow about 30 seconds for children to write the answer to each, before moving on to the next question.

1 Write this number: ninety thousand and nine. *90,009*

2 520 + 99 = *619*

3 What is 0.2 more than 0.19? *0.39*

4 12 + ? = 20 *8*

5 125 + ? = 200 *75*

6 36 + ? = 100 *64*

7 350 + ? = 1000 *650*

8 640 + ? = 1000 *360*

9 1.2 + ? = 2.0 *0.8*

10 15 – 8 = *7*

11 43 – 7 = *36*

12 135 – 28 = *107*

13 355 – 155 = *200*

14 264 – 99 = *165*

15 42 × 4 = *168*

16 4 × 60 = *240*

17 7 × 21 = *147*

18 half of 1286 = *643*

19 double 104 *208*

20 25% of 10 000 is...? *2,500*

Number of the week

Sample tasks
- Can our number be divided exactly by 2, by 3, by 4 , ...?
- Name pairs of numbers which multiply to make our number.
- What is the third, tenth, sixth, ... multiple of our number?

Sample facts
- it is a multiple of 2, of 4, of 5, of 8, of 10, of 20 and of 40
- 40 years is 4 decades
- it is 25% of 160

Word of the week

Sample tasks
- What is the square root of 49? The **square root** of 49 is 7.
- Use your calculator to find the **square root** of 18. The **square root** of 18 is about 4.24.

Sample facts
- square numbers have a whole number **square root**
- the **square root** of 1 is 1
- $\sqrt{\ }$ is the symbol for **square root**

Shape of the week

Sample facts
- a trapezium is a type of quadrilateral
- a trapezium has one pair of parallel sides
- more than two trapeziums are called trapezia
- a trapezium has one less pair of parallel sides than a parallelogram

- a trapezium whose non-parallel sides are equal is called an isosceles trapezium

N27 Division

Table timer

Multiplying by 4, 7 and 14
Draw a table with four columns. In the first
column write numbers up to 12 at random.
Children copy the table, multiplying by 4 and
writing the answers in the second column, by
7 in the third column and by 14 in the third
column. Time them.

	x 4	x 7	x 14
8			
12			

Three in a row

Dividing a 3-digit multiple of 10 by a 2-digit multiple of 10
Four small number grids (1 to 100), counters
Divide the class into four teams, and give each team a number grid and
some counters.
Write a division on the board – a 3-digit multiple of 10 by a 2-digit
multiple of 10, e.g. 460 ÷ 20.
Choose a child to say the answer.
If the child answers correctly the team can cover that number on their
grid with a counter.
Continue, choosing a child from each team in turn. The winner is the
first team to place three counters in any row or column.

All wrong

Dividing by 200, 300, 400
Write ten divisions on the board
– a 4-digit multiple of 100 by a
3-digit multiple of 100. Ensure
that they are all incorrect.
Point to a division, and choose
several children to say why it is
incorrect, and what the correct answer should be.
Repeat for each division.

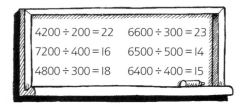

4200 ÷ 200 = 22	6600 ÷ 300 = 23
7200 ÷ 400 = 16	6500 ÷ 500 = 14
4800 ÷ 300 = 18	6400 ÷ 400 = 15

Bingo

Addition bonds to 1000
Each pair writes five bingo numbers that are multiples of 50 up to 1000.
Write a multiple of 50 on the board, e.g. 250. Choose a child to say the
addition bond to 1000. Any pair with a matching number can cross it
out.

i d w u l n e r f
2 4 1 8 9.3 5 6 7

Codes

Dividing a 3-digit by a 2-digit number

Number cards (0 to 9), one set per pair

Write these coded divisions on the board:

ido ÷ wo = id	ero ÷ wo = er	uuo ÷ do = ii	rro ÷ no = ii
ddo ÷ io = ii	iio ÷ io = ww	eeo ÷ eo = ww	eoo ÷ io = ie
foo ÷ io = ne	llo ÷ no = nn		

Each digit (0 to 9) is represented by one letter only. 0 is represented by o.
Allow the children five minutes to explore the code.
Discuss the solution.

Number of the week

Sample tasks
- Divide each of these by our number: 24, 48, 16, 32, 88, 160, ...
- Continue halving from our number: 8, 4, 2, ...
- Continue doubling from our number: 8, 16, 32, ...
- What is 25%, 50%, 75%, of our number.

Sample facts
- it has 4 factors: 1, 2, 4, 8
- it is the number of sides of an octagon, legs of an octopus
- it is the number of hours in one third of a day

Word of the week

Sample tasks
- What is the **mode** of: 5, 6, 6, 6, 7, 7, 8? The **mode** is 6.
- Find the **mode** for the shoe sizes in our class. The **mode** is $3\frac{1}{2}$.
- For the data 3, 4, 4, 5, 9, which is the larger: the mean, median or **mode**? The **mode** is 4, the median is 4, the mean is 5.

Sample facts
- the **mode** is a type of average, alongside mean and median
- in a set of observations, the **mode** is the one which occurs most often
- for data on the frequency of each letter in a page of text, the **mode** is usually letter 'e'

N28 Problem solving

Show me

Doubling decimals (hundredths)
Number cards (0 to 9), one set per pair
Set the children tasks where they have to match a particular criterion
using the cards. For example:
Show me double 1.3, 1.15, 2.5, 1.55, 1.99, ...

Table timer

Addition bonds to 100 and 1000
Draw two tables with two
columns. In the first table write
2-digit numbers at random in
the first column. In the second
table write 3-digit multiples of
10 at random in the first column.

	Make 100
14	
41	

	Make 1000
342	
810	

Children copy the table, writing the addition bond to 100 and the
addition bond to 1000 in the correct table. Time them.

Missing numbers

Adding, subtracting, dividing
Write ten equations on the board,
each using more than one
operation. In each case replace
one of the numbers with a '?'.
Point to a missing number and
choose a child to say what it is.
Repeat for each missing number.

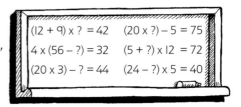

$(12 + 9) \times ? = 42$ $(20 \times ?) - 5 = 75$

$4 \times (56 - ?) = 32$ $(5 + ?) \times 12 = 72$

$(20 \times 3) - ? = 44$ $(24 - ?) \times 5 = 40$

Target number

Doubling, adding and subtracting
Write a target number on the board, e.g. 66.
Each pair works to find a way of making the target by doubling
(a decimal number with 5 tenths), then adding or subtracting
(e.g. double 19.5 = 39, 39 + 27 = 66). Ask different pairs for their
solutions. Discuss the different ways. Repeat for a new target.

Twenty questions

Place-value, adding, subtracting, doubling, multiplying, halving
Read out these numbered questions, writing them on the board as you

read them. Allow about 30 seconds for children to write the answer to each, before moving on to the next question.

1 Write this number: ten thousand and sixty-four.   **2** $32 - 7 =$
3 What is 0.02 more than 9.99?   **4** $151 - 8 =$
5 $382 - 199 =$ **6** $3.4 - 1.9 =$ **7** $1000 - 550 =$
8 $100 - 34 =$ **9** $5.0 - 2.4 =$ **10** $14.6 - 8.6 =$
11 $99 \times 3 =$ **12** double 199   **13** $6 + 9 + 13 + 7 + 4 =$
14 $360 \div 40 =$ **15** $35 \div 4 =$ **16** $74 \div 9 =$
17 $120 \div 5 =$ **18** 42% of 200 =   **19** $440 + 660 =$
20 Write fourteen hundredths as a decimal.

Number of the week

Sample tasks
- What is... double our number, add 3/treble our number, subtract 5, ...?
- What is 20%, 50%, 60%, ... of our number?
- What is the square number before and after our number?

Sample facts
- it is a quarter century
- it is the fifth square number, having a square root of 5
- It has an odd number of factors – 3 factors: 1, 5, 25

Word of the week

reflex angle

Sample tasks
- Is 260° a **reflex angle**? Yes it is a reflex angle.
- How many **reflex angles** can a triangle have? A triangle cannot have any **reflex angles**.
- When turning through a **reflex angle** a clock's minute hand must move more than 30 minutes and less than 1 hour.

Sample facts
- a **reflex angle** is an angle more than 2 right angles and less than 4 right angles
- turning clockwise from facing North to face West is turning through a **reflex angle**
- if a quadrilateral has a **reflex angle**, then it is concave (it 'caves' in)

Shape of the week

segment of a circle

Sample facts
- two segments of a circle are made by slicing anywhere across the circle
- drawing a chord of a circle creates two segments
- a segment of a circle has 2 sides: a straight side

(chord) and a curved side (arc)
- a segment whose straight side is a diameter is a semi-circle
- a straight line joining the ends of the arc of a circle creates a chord

N29 Multiplication

All wrong

*Adding to a 3-digit number to
make the next hundred*
Write ten additions on the board,
of a 3-digit number to the next
hundred. Ensure that they are
all incorrect.

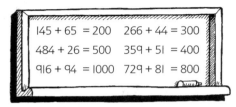

145 + 65 = 200	266 + 44 = 300
484 + 26 = 500	359 + 51 = 400
916 + 94 = 1000	729 + 81 = 800

Point to an addition, and choose several children to say why it is
incorrect, and what the correct answer should be.
Repeat for each addition.

Grid multiplication

Multiplying a decimal (tenths) by 10
Draw a 2 × 5 grid on the board, with a decimal number (tenths) up to 12
in each space.
Children copy the grid, multiplying each number by 10.
When the grid is complete, point to each space in turn, asking a
different child to say their answer.

Make me

Adding and multiplying
Write 3.4, 10, 5.7, 100 on the board, each in a triangle.
Write 604, 397, 1910, 9100 on the board, each in a circle.
The children can combine any or all of the triangle numbers by adding
or multiplying.
Can they make any of the circle numbers?
Allow ten minutes. Discuss the different answers.

Bingo

Multiplying decimals (hundredths) by 10
Number cards (0 to 9)
Each pair writes five bingo numbers that are decimals (tenths) between
10 and 20.
Select two cards at random (one for tenths, one for hundredth). Make a
decimal number with one unit, e.g. 1.48, 1.57.
Choose a child to multiply by 10.
Any pair with a matching number can cross it out.
The winner is the first pair to cross out three of their numbers.

Open the box

Multiplying decimals (hundredths) by 100
Draw a 2 × 5 grid on the board. Cover each space with a multiplication of a decimal (hundredths) by 100. Underneath write the answer.
Choose a child to point to a box and say the answer.
Check with the class.
The child can 'open the box', to reveal the answer.

Number of the week

Sample tasks
- Multiply 1.7, 3.6, 4.8, 11.2, ... by our number.
- Multiply 1.34, 2.45, 3.67, 4.08, ... by our number.
- Multiply our number by 2.3, 1.76, 0.45, 40, ...

Sample facts
- it is the tenth square number, having a square root of 10
- it is the number of centimetres in a metre, pence in a pound
- when a number is multiplied by our number its digits slide 2 places to the left

---

Word of the week

Sample tasks
- Show me the horizontal **axis** on this graph. This is the horizontal **axis**.
- Mark a point on the vertical **axis** and say its coordinates. My point on the vertical **axis** has coordinates (0, 5).
- On which **axis** lies the point (4, 0)? (4, 0) lies on the horizontal **axis**.

Sample facts
- a graph has a horizontal **axis** and a vertical **axis**
- **axes** must be labelled
- points on the horizontal **axis** of a coordinate grid have a second coordinate of zero

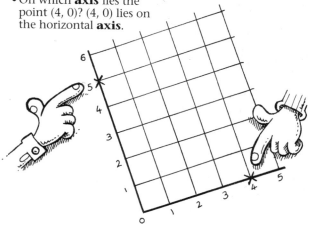

 Multiplication

Table timer

Multiplying decimals by 2, 3 and 10
Draw a table with four columns. In the first
column write decimal numbers (tenths) up to
12 at random. Children copy the table,
multiplying by 2 and writing the answer in
the second column, by 3 in the third column
and by 10 in the fourth column. Time them.

	x 2	x 3	x 10
6			
5			

Money

Decimals (hundredths)
Coins (2p, 5p, 10p, 20p, 50p, £1) (or cards marked with these amounts)
Tell the class that the Royal Mint has decided to withdraw the 1p coin.
Which amounts of money will it now be impossible to make?
Encourage them to record the amounts as decimals (e.g. 28p is £0.28).
You may wish to give each pair sets of coins to help them (2p, 5p, 10p,
20p, 50p, £1). Allow ten minutes, then discuss the different answers.

Missing numbers

*Multiplying a decimal (tenths) by a
1-digit number*
Write ten multiplications on the
board, of a decimal number
(tenths) by a 1-digit number. In
each case replace one of the
digits or numbers with a '?'.

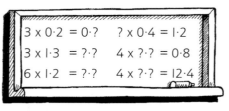

$3 \times 0.2 = 0.?$ $? \times 0.4 = 1.2$
$3 \times 1.3 = ?.?$ $4 \times ?.? = 0.8$
$6 \times 1.2 = ?.?$ $4 \times ?.? = 12.4$

Point to a missing number and choose a child to say what it is.
Repeat for each missing number.

Codes

Multiplying a decimal (tenths) by a 1-digit number
Number cards (0 to 9) one set per pair
In pairs the children design a code based on multiplying decimals
(tenths) by a 1-digit number. They replace digits with letters,
e.g. $3.2 \times 2 = 6.4$ can become $a.b \times b = c.d$. Each digit (0 to 9) is
represented by one letter only. Allow the children five minutes to
compose the code, then swap with their neighbours. After five minutes,
discuss the different codes.

Twenty questions

Place-value, adding, subtracting, doubling, multiplying, halving
Read out these numbered questions, writing them on the board as you read them. Allow about 30 seconds for children to write the answer to each, before moving on to the next question.

1 Write this number: one hundred and one thousand, one hundred and one.
2 What is 0.02 less than 0.5? **3** 3.2 × 4 = **4** 4 × 6.6 =
5 3.1 – 1.9 = **6** 4.3 + 2.7 = **7** 10 × 30 =
8 23 × 4 = **9** 480 + 520 = **10** 43 – 7 =
11 143 – 136 = **12** 283 – 199 = **13** 42 + 43 + 44 =
14 9 × 25 = **16** 200 × 30 = **17** 2.3 × 10 =
18 4.21 × 10 = **19** Write $\frac{2}{5}$ as a decimal **20** Find 40% of 200

| **Number of the week**  | **Sample tasks** • Multiply our number by 2, by 3, by 5, by 6, ... • Continue doubling our number: 1.2, 2.4, 4.8, ... • Say our number as fraction. | **Sample facts** • it is between 1 and 2, but nearer 1 • it is one half of 2.4, one quarter of 4.8, one fifth of 6 • it is 12 tenths, or 1 whole and 2 tenths |

| **Word of the week** | **Sample tasks** • How many **millimetres** in 4.5 centimetres? There are 45 **millimetres** in 4.5 centimetres. • Draw a line 67 **millimetres** long. • Estimate this length in **millimetres**. I estimate its length to be 150 **millimetres**. | **Sample facts** • a **millimetre** is a metric unit of length • there are 10 **millimetres** in 1 centimetre • there are 1000 **millimetres** in 1 metre |

Shape of the week

irregular polygon

Sample facts
• a polygon whose sides are not all equal is called an irregular polygon
• an irregular polygon will have angles which are not all equal

• an irregular polygon is a non-regular polygon
• a rhombus is an irregular polygon
• an isosceles triangle is an irregular polygon

N31 Division

Table timer

Multiplying decimals by 2, 10 and 100
Draw a table with four columns. In the first
column write decimal numbers up to 10 at
random. Children copy the table, multiplying
by 2 and writing the answer in the second
column, by 10 in the third column and by
100 in the fourth column.
Time them.

	x 2	x 10	x 100
1.5			
3.4			
0.6			

All wrong

Dividing a 2-digit number by 10
Write ten divisions on the board, Î
of a 2-digit number by 10.
Ensure that they are all incorrect.
Point to a division, and choose
several children to say why it is
incorrect, and what the correct answer should be.
Repeat for each division.

$43 \div 10 = 0.43$ $23 \div 10 = 0.23$
$72 \div 100 = 7.2$ $42 \div 10 = 4.2$
$32 \div 10 = 0.032$ $90 \div 10 = 0.09$

Target number

Dividing, adding and subtracting
Write a decimal target number on the board, e.g. 5.5.
Each pair works to find a way of making the target by dividing a 2-digit
number by 10, then adding or subtracting (e.g. $62 \div 10 = 6.2$,
$6.2 - 0.7 = 5.5$).
Ask different pairs for their solutions. Discuss the different ways.
Repeat for a new target.

Bingo

Adding two decimals that make a whole number
Number cards (0 to 9)
Each pair writes five bingo numbers from 1 to 10.
Select two cards at random. Make a decimal number (tenths), and write
it on the board, e.g. 4.3. Add a second decimal that will give a whole
number answer, e.g. 4.3 + 2.7.
Choose a child to say the answer.
Any pair with a matching number can cross it out.

Three in a row

Subtracting a 1-digit from a 2-digit number

Four small number grids (1 to 100), counters, large number grid (1 to 100)

Divide the class into four teams, and give each team a number grid and some counters.

Point to a 2-digit number and a 1-digit number on the large grid, e.g. 46 and 8. Choose a child to say the difference between the two numbers. If the child answers correctly the team can cover either of the two numbers on their grid with a counter.

Continue, choosing a child from each team in turn. The winner is the first team to place three counters in any row or column.

Number of the week

Sample tasks
- Divide 50, 24, 35, 68, 93, 135, 247, ... by our number.
- Multiply 2.5, 4.6, 7.7, 12.8, ...by our number.
- Divide these numbers by 10, then by 10 again: 456, 382, 760, ...

Sample facts
- it is one tenth of a hundred, one hundredth of a thousand
- it is the number of years in a decade, sides on a decagon, events in a decathlon
- when a number is divided by our number its digits slide 1 place to the right

---

Word of the week

Sample tasks
- What is the **probability** that this dice will land '3'? The **probability** is $\frac{1}{6}$.
- What is the **probability** that this coin will land 'heads'? The **probability** is $\frac{1}{2}$.
- If we throw two dice, the total can be 2, 3, 4, ..., 12. Do these totals each have the same **probability**? No, their **probabilities** are not the same. For example, a total of '7' has a greater **probability** than the other totals.

Sample facts
- the **probability** of an event is a matching from the event to a point on the number line from 0 to 1
- a **probability** can only be between 0 and 1 inclusive
- an 'even' chance has a **probability** of $\frac{1}{2}$ or 0.5

 Division

Table timer

Multiplying by 3, 6 and 9
Draw a table with four columns. In the first
column write numbers up to 15 at random.
Children copy the table, multiplying by 3 and
writing the answer in the second column, by 6
in the third column and by 9 in the fourth
column. Time them.

	x 3	x 6	x 9
15			
3			

Grid division

Dividing a 2- or 3-digit number by a 1-digit number (with remainders)
Draw a 2 × 5 grid on the board, with a 2- or 3-digit number in
each space.
Children copy the grid, dividing each number by 7 and writing the
answer and any remainder.
When the grid is complete, point to each space in turn, asking a
different child to say their answer.
Repeat for dividing by 9, 8, 6, ...

Make me

Adding, dividing
Write 6, 39, 3, 84 on the board, each in a
triangle. Write 27, 32.5, 1, 19.5, 13 on
the board, each in a circle. The children
can combine any or all of the triangle
numbers by adding or dividing.
Can they make any of the circle
numbers? Allow ten minutes.
Discuss the different answers.

Open the box

Dividing by 9
Draw a 2 × 5 grid on the board. Cover each space with a division of a
2- or 3-digit number by 9. Underneath write the answer.
Choose a child to point to a box and say the answer (they can work on
the board to help). Check with the class.
The child can 'open the box', to reveal the answer.

Twenty questions

Place-value, adding, subtracting, doubling, multiplying, halving
Read out these numbered questions, writing them on the board as you read them. Allow about 30 seconds for children to write the answer to each, before moving on to the next question.

1 Write this number: one hundred and twenty-four thousand, six hundred and six.   **2** What is two-more than 99 999?

3 $2.7 + 6.3 =$	**4** $34 \times 5 =$	**5** $5.2 - 3 =$
6 $2.5 \times 6 =$	**7** $38 \div 6 =$	**8** $121 - 31 =$
9 $1000 - 23 =$	**10** $425 - 326 =$	**11** $52 - 46 =$
12 $1793 + 300 =$	**13** $4 \times 8 =$	**14** $4 \times 16 =$
15 $370 \times 2 =$	**16** $420 \div 7 =$	**17** $\frac{3}{4}$ of $48 =$
18 50% of 4.5 =	**19** $6.2 \times 4 =$	**20** $(12 \times 4) - 8 =$

Number of the week

Sample tasks
- Divide our number by 4, by 5, by 6, ...
- What do you have to divide our number by to have remainder of 4?
- What are the factors of our number?

Sample facts
- it is a prime number
- it is the number of days in several months e.g. January
- its reverse (13) is also a prime number

Word of the week

Sample tasks
- Use your **set square** to draw a right-angle.
- Check if these are right angles using your **set square**. My **set square** shows that these are right angles and these are not.
- Use your **set square** to check if this angle is more or less than 30°. My **set square** shows that it is less than 30°.

Sample facts
- a **set square** is an instrument for drawing and measuring right-angles
- some **set squares** have angles of 60°, 30°, 90° and some have angles 45°, 45°, 90°
- a **set square** can be used to draw parallel lines by sliding it along a ruler

---

Shape of the week

Sample facts
- a polyhedron is a 3-d solid shape
- a cube and cuboid are types of polyhedrons (polyhedra)
- an 8-faced polyhedron is called an octahedron.
- a 4-faced polyhedron is called a tetrahedron
- a polyhedron has faces which are polygons

Skills Chart

The chart on the following pages outlines all the mental skills addressed by the Mental Warm-up Activities. The skills are divided into three key areas: place-value and number, addition and subtraction, multiplication and division. Within each section, the skills are arranged by topic, e.g. counting, addition bonds, multiplication facts. The generic activities 'Target number', 'Make me' and 'Twenty questions' are specifically written to cover a range of skills, and so are not included in this chart.

The chart will assist any teacher looking for an activity dealing with a specific skill. It also makes clear the build-up and sequence of concepts covered throughout the book.

Place-value and Number

Topic	Specific Skills	Units
Counting	Counting 5-digit numbers	N1
	Counting on one from a 5-digit number	N1
	Counting decimal numbers	N2
	Counting back one hundredth from a decimal number	N3
Number	Finding factors	N22
	Square numbers	N21
	Squaring multiples of 10	N21
	Equations	N24
Rounding	Rounding a 3-digit number to the nearest hundred	N6
	Rounding a 4-digit number to the nearest thousand	N25
	Rounding a decimal (tenths) to the nearest whole number	N4, N10
	Rounding a decimal (hundredths) to the nearest tenth	N4
	Rounding a decimal (hundredths) to the nearest whole number	N4, N10
Fractions, decimals and percentages	Finding halves	N16
	Finding quarters	N16
	Equivalent fractions	N16, N17
	Finding 10%	N19
	Finding percentages	N18, N19
	Fractions, decimals and percentages	N18
	Decimal fractions	N3, N18
	Decimals (hundredths)	N2, N4, N7, N30

Addition and Subtraction

Topic	Specific skills	Units
Addition bonds	Addition bonds to 20 and 100	N1
	Addition bonds to 50 and 100	N5
	Addition bonds to 100	N1, N3, N5, N11, N12, N14
	Addition bonds to 100 and 1000	N7, N25, N28
	Addition bonds to 1000	N5, N26, N27
	Addition bonds to 1.00 and 2.00	N11
The next ten, hundred, tenth, whole number	Adding to a 3-digit number to make the next hundred	N29
	Adding to a decimal (tenths) to make the next whole number	N12
	Adding to a decimal (hundredths) to make the next whole number	N10, N11, N12
Estimating addition	Estimating the addition of three 2- or 3-digit numbers	N6
	Estimating the addition of two 4-digit numbers	N6
	Estimating the addition of two decimals (tenths)	N10
Addition 2- and 3-digit numbers	Adding multiples of 10	N5
	Adding near doubles	N11
	Adding to make multiples of 1000	N25
	Adding two 2-digit multiples of 10	N5
	Adding two 3-digit numbers	N21
Adding decimals	Adding two decimals (tenths)	N11
	Adding two decimals that make a whole number	N31
	Adding positive and negative numbers	N7
	Adding several 1- and 2-digit numbers	N22
	Adding several 1-digit numbers	N6

Subtraction		
	Subtracting a 1-digit from a 2-digit number	N25, N31
	Subtracting 99 from a 3-digit number	N15
	Subtracting one 2-digit number from another by counting on	N2, N21
	Subtracting near multiples of 100 from a 3-digit number	N13

Multiplication and Division

Topic	Specific Skills	Units
Multiplication facts	Multiplication facts up to 10 x 10	N8, N9
	Multiplying by 2, 4 and 8	N3, N17
	Multiplying by 3, 6 and 12	N19, N23
	Multiplying by 3, 6 and 9	N32
	Multiplying by 4, 7 and 14	N27
	Multiplying by 4, 8 and 16	N8
	Multiplying by 5, 10 and 100	N13
	Multiplying by 5, 10 and 20	N21
	Multiplying by 8	N2
	Doubling decimals (hundredths)	N28
Multiplying 2- and 3- digit numbers	Multiplying a 2- or 3-digit number by a 1-digit number	N14
	Multiplying a 2-digit by a 1-digit number	N14, N20
	Multiplying a 3-digit by a 1-digit number	N15
	Multiplying a 3-digit multiple of 10 by a 1-digit number	N20
	Multiplying a 3-digit number by 2 or 3	N8
	Multiplying by 10 and multiples of 10	N13
	Multiplying by 20, 50 and 100	N15
	Multiplying by 200, 300 and 400	N13, N20
	Multiplying by multiples of 100	N13

Multiplying decimals	Multiplying a decimal (tenths) by 10	N29
	Multiplying a decimal (tenths) by a 1-digit number	N30
	Multiplying a decimal (hundredths) by 10	N15
	Multiplying decimals (hundredths) by 10	N29
	Multiplying decimals (hundredths) by 100	N29
	Multiplying decimals by 2, 10 and 100	N31
	Multiplying decimals by 2, 3 and 10	N30
Division facts	Dividing by 9	N9, N32
	Divisibility rules	N23
Dividing 2- and 3-digit numbers	Dividing a 2-digit by a 1-digit number	N9, N15, N22, N24
	Dividing a 2-digit number by 10	N31
	Dividing a 2- or 3-digit number by a 1-digit number (with remainders)	N26, N32
	Dividing a 3-digit multiples of 10 by a 2-digit multiple of 10	
	Dividing a multiple of 100 by a 1- or 2-digit number	N27
	Dividing a 3-digit by a 2-digit number	N17
	Dividing by 2, 3 and 4	N27
	Dividing by 200, 300, 400	N23
	Estimating the division of a 3-digit by a 2-digit number	N27
		N24